# clic
## INTERNATIONAL™

# STUDENT STYLIST
# COURSEBOOK

Permission requests should be sent in writing to the following address:
CLIC INTERNATIONAL®
396 Pottsville / Saint Clair Highway
Pottsville, PA 17901 USA

ISBN 978-0-9761358-7-6

# YOUR STUDENT STYLIST
# coursebook

Your coursebook is a tool designed to enhance your understanding of the textbook material and to reinforce classroom learning. Activities have been designed to help you review, process, and expand upon concepts introduced in the textbook.

You are encouraged to thoroughly use your textbook as you complete your coursebook. Locate the source of the topics / activities, highlight, take notes, ask questions. We have included at least one page in each section that is entitled 'My Need to Know Notes'. Use this section for *you* – to write reminders, what you learned, what you don't understand, goals you have – whatever you need.

As you successfully complete each chapter, you will find a puzzle piece. Each piece represents one step – a step that means you are closer to becoming a licensed professional. You are creating a symbolic certificate that will one day become a real one – one you will display at your salon station with pride and accomplishment.

Although each learning activity is unique, we can give you some general insight into how to complete each activity. Questions and answers are based upon the 'Need to Know' and Bolded terminology found throughout the chapter.

# DIRECTIONS FOR EXERCISES:

## Matching
Match each word to its definition. Definitions may be phrased a little differently than in the text, but we want you to understand and be comfortable seeing different versions of the definitions.

## Fill In the Blank
Complete the phrase or sentence with the correct term or phrase. Content that is located on the same page in the textbook will not have a word bank; find and refer to the page(s) in the text for the terminology that you will use as your answers.

## Open-Ended Exercises
You will find many activities where we ask you to 'Describe', 'Explain', 'Discuss'. The purpose of these questions is for you to put important terms into your own words. If you can explain concepts to yourself and others, you understand the information!

## Word Search
We've provided you with the definition, you provide the answer. Have fun finding a word after you identify the term described. Words can be found in any direction: horizontally, vertically, diagonally, and backwards.

## Crossword
Use the terminology found in the textbook to complete the puzzle. Do not include spaces or punctuation for two word or hyphenated words. For example, *non-verbal* would be included in the puzzle as *nonverbal* or *active listening* would be written as *activelistening*.

## Diagram
Diagrams are visual tools to help you remember placement. Label the important parts identified or complete the 'mental picture' of a concept.

## Head Diagrams
Use the diagrams found throughout the coursebook to brainstorm, sketch, plan, design and prepare for techniques you are learning.

## Charts
Charts are a quick and easy way to describe, categorize, organize, compare and/or contrast information. Complete all blank categories / boxes for any charts provided.

## Multiple Choice

Choose the best answer from those provided. Carefully read the question – sometimes one or two words in the question can be the key to the answer. If you think there may be two possible answers, choose the one that you think best fits.

## Workshop Standards

We've compiled what we think are the most important steps to a service(s). The more you practice, the more you improve. The key is to first meet the expectations of the skill set – that's why the only option is 'Met Skill'. If you don't satisfactorily complete the skill, practice until you do.

## Situational Scenarios

After you've learned all technical information, we'd like to place you into a 'real-world' situation. Some questions may be more difficult to answer than others, as dealing with Guests and providing Guest Service doesn't have a 'one size fits all' answer. Use these situations to spark conversations and to plan in your mind what you would do if the situation occurred.

## Practical Prep

Knowing the end result and expectations is essential as you work through each chapter. We included all the steps required to complete the skill. We want you, at minimum, to be proficient at the essential services. However, see this as a starting point – your Guest Service Skills and creativity will determine your ultimate success.

## State Board

Although this exercise may not be your favorite, it is a really important piece of your puzzle. Questions and answers have been carefully chosen to prepare you for your State Boards. Stick with this exercise – use it as a guide to see how prepared you are for your written exam.

The more you read, practice, and work with concepts in the textbook and coursebook, the more growth and success you will have, and the closer you will be to becoming a licensed professional and fulfilling your dream.

# BEST OF LUCK!

# DEPARTMENT OF STATE

## BUREAU OF PROFESSIONAL & OCCUPATIONAL AFFAIRS

PO Box 396 State 12345

*Cosmetology License*

SAMPLE NAME
123 ANY STREET
CITY, STATE 12345

INITIAL LICENSE DATE
01/1/2014

EXPIRATION DATE
01/31/2016

Commissioner of Professional & Occupational Affairs

№ 569403

LICENSE STATUS: ACTIVE

NAIL CARE

SKIN CARE

DESIGN PRINCIPLES

# PATHWAY TO
# SUCCESS

# MY NEED TO KNOW notes:

'80 to 20' Formula for success
80% excellent people skills
20% superb technical skills

Retention Rate: Retain 1 out of every 4 new Guest

# STEPS TO SUCCESS

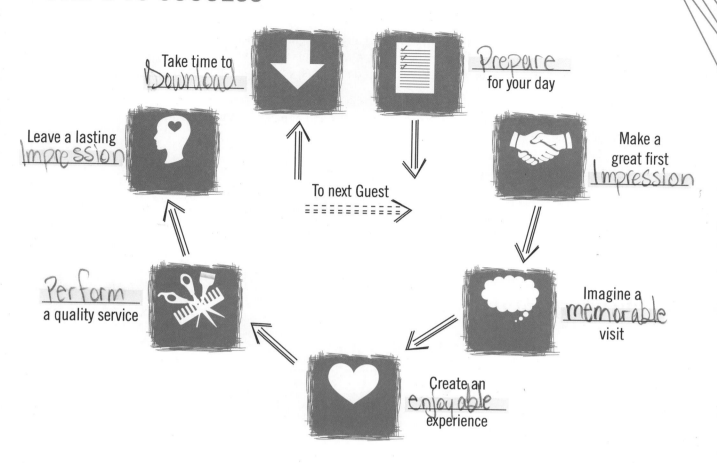

Take time to Download

Prepare for your day

Leave a lasting Impression

Make a great first Impression

To next Guest

Perform a quality service

Imagine a memorable visit

Create an enjoyable experience

## Successful stylists have the ability to do the following:

**RETAIN**

Guest Retention is the loyalty Guests show you by continuously returning for services.

**ATTRACT**

Guest Referral is the ability to attract new Guests through your existing Guests.

**MANAGE**

_____ is scheduling your Guest's next appointment prior to them leaving your salon.

**MASTER**

Guest Service Cycle is a blueprint used to ensure a great Guest experience at each stage of your Guest's visit.

Learning the above skills will help you become a successful stylist. Preparing for your day and setting your _____, a target that is planned, monitored and reached, will benefit you and reduce any potentional _____, which is your physical and psychological response to demanding situations.

# SETTING GOALS

You are saving to purchase a car. You have totaled all your monthly expenses and have come up with a weekly service goal of $900.00, working 5 days a week. This will provide you enough money to pay monthly expenses and save for your new car. On a daily basis, your service goal is $_____.

In order to achieve and maintain this daily goal, you will need to be creative in time management and scheduling appointments. Utilizing the service price list and appointment book page, how can you achieve your daily goal?

**INTERESTING FACT:** Some salons offer Guests a discounted haircut with a Chemical Service.

| SERVICE PRICE LIST | |
| --- | --- |
| HAIRCUT | $20 |
| CHILD'S HAIRCUT | $12 |
| HAIRCUT W/ CHEMICAL SERVICE | $10 |
| HAIRCOLOR | $25 |
| HIGHLIGHT | $30 |
| PERMANENT WAVE | $30 |
| WAXING | $10 |
| MANICURE | $15 |
| PEDICURE | $25 |
| DEEP CONDITIONING TREATMENT | $10 |

# MEETING YOUR GOAL

|  | |  |
|---|---|---|
| **9**am | :00 | UTILIZE CANCELLATION LIST |
| | :30 | |
| **10**am | :00 | Mary – haircolor |
| | :30 | |
| **11**am | :00 | |
| | :30 | UTILIZE CANCELLATION LIST |
| **12**pm | :00 | |
| | :30 | |
| **1**pm | :00 | Lunch |
| | :30 | Jim – haircut |
| **2**pm | :00 | Jimmy – child haircut |
| | :30 | |
| **3**pm | :00 | Tina – eyebrow wax |
| | :30 | OPPORTUNITY TO UP-SELL |
| **4**pm | :00 | Betty – permanent wave, haircut, and style |
| | :30 | |
| **5**pm | :00 | |
| | :30 | |
| **6**pm | :00 | OPPORTUNITY TO UP-SELL |
| | :30 | |
| **7**pm | :00 | Sarah – haircolor / highlight / haircut |
| | :30 | |
| **8**pm | :00 | |
| | :30 | |
| **9**pm | :00 | |
| | :30 | |

// Calculating your pre-booked appointments for the day, you have $_____ towards your daily goal.

// Sarah, your 7:00 pm appointment, called and cancelled. Recalculating your pre-booked appointments, you now have $_____.

**In order to remain on target, what marketing techniques can you utilize to reach your daily goal?**

// The action of selling additional services and/or products based on need and solutions is _____.

// A _____ _____ contains the information on your Guests who are not able to book an appointment when requested and want an appointment as soon as possible.

**This list should contain the following information:**

1. _____
2. _____
3. _____
4. _____

// Giving your Guests a higher level of Guest service than what is offered by competitors creates a _____.

// Directing your marketing efforts towards individuals who you want to purchase your services and products is known as _____ _____.

# IT'S ALL ABOUT A POSITIVE IMPRESSION

"You have only one chance to make a great _____ impression."

A person's overall evaluation of their self-worth is their _____ _____.
Not only should you be aware of your own self-esteem, but your Guest's as well. Your behavior, communication and appearance all play an important part to your success.

To be successful, you must _____ and _____ professional. This is known as your _____ _____.

Your _____ _____ is a daily routine to maintain your body's cleanliness. This includes your bodily and oral hygiene.

Your appearance is a billboard of you. The message you want to send to your Guests is reflected not only through your attitude but also your appearance. _____ is a 'mental imprint' that belongs to a product, service, event and/or individual.

Your visual message should appeal to your target-market Guests. _____ _____ is your attempt to ensure only positive impressions of you are perceived by your Guests.

Based on your appearance and professionalism, you should always stand out in a crowd as a professional stylist. This will help you to gain new Guests and build a strong Guest following. Utilizing social settings as an opportunity to meet and gain new Guests is known as _____.

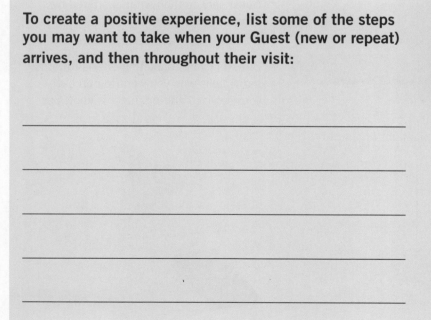

**To create a positive experience, list some of the steps you may want to take when your Guest (new or repeat) arrives, and then throughout their visit:**

_____

_____

_____

_____

_____

# BODY LANGUAGE

**What does body language or gestures tell you about a person: their mood, feelings, personality?**

Beside each picture, describe your perception of the person(s) in the photo. Then compare with your classmates and discuss the similarities and differences.

1. _____

_____

_____

2. _____

_____

3. _____

_____

4. _____

_____

_____

5. _____

_____

6. _____

_____

_____

7. _____

_____

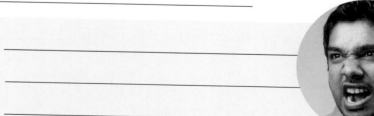

8. _____

_____

# COMMUNICATION CREATES SUCCESS | WORD SEARCH

1. Using verbal and non-verbal signs to show your Guest that you are interested is _____.

2. Communication cues you provide with your body movement and position are _____.

3. Being able to answer with a simple *yes* or *no* is a _____ – _____ question.

4. Eye movement, your posture and appearance are all signs of _____ – _____ communication.

5. Having to use more than one or two words to answer is an _____ – _____ question.

6. Repeating what your Guest told you using your own words is _____.

7. Products that are sold to your Guest based on their needs is _____.

8. The process of obtaining information you need from your Guest to make service and product recommendation is _____.

```
R  N  P  L  N  X  N  N  D  P  H  F  W  M  C  F  N  R
N  N  R  G  K  X  G  C  X  H  H  P  T  Q  H  C  O  C
M  Q  C  L  O  S  E  D  E  N  D  E  D  R  W  Z  N  L
K  X  M  W  G  V  E  R  B  A  L  K  L  T  D  R  V  M
R  L  W  R  N  J  L  T  Y  Z  N  D  F  R  L  E  H  H
W  T  M  M  I  D  M  N  J  R  N  Y  L  S  T  G  R  N
N  C  C  J  N  X  J  M  F  D  L  J  E  Y  A  G  B  C
N  G  O  L  E  R  G  L  J  K  F  I  J  U  L  N  A  T
J  T  L  N  T  D  N  R  Z  V  L  R  G  R  D  I  L  D
P  V  V  L  S  Z  C  K  Y  P  J  N  R  T  T  S  Z  T
R  N  V  V  I  U  T  F  P  R  A  D  P  Q  L  A  N  L
B  K  L  T  L  U  L  U  L  L  V  L  N  O  B  R  G  T
H  J  Q  K  E  V  S  T  Y  G  C  V  P  S  N  N  H  L
V  H  F  R  V  L  P  D  A  B  D  E  Z  P  F  P  N  C
N  J  H  V  I  X  O  V  G  T  N  Q  C  C  B  A  Y  P
L  C  N  A  T  B  K  B  M  E  I  K  K  L  B  R  C  Q
M  F  T  M  C  K  M  P  N  L  L  O  C  J  W  A  L  D
T  E  R  Y  A  K  M  D  L  H  Z  F  N  B  G  P  C  H
R  N  P  K  K  K  E  W  J  P  T  V  M  N  X  F  B  W
T  T  N  R  H  D  D  B  J  B  L  F  G  Q  W  L  G  Q
```

# CREATE AN ENJOYABLE, QUALITY SERVICE

The principles that guide your professional behavior are known as _____.
Displaying these principles will show your professionalism.

Before, during and after your Guest service, always be sure to dedicate yourself to _____.

**Give examples of the steps you can take to show your _____, which is behaving in a manner appropriate for the business setting.**

# SHOW ME THE $$$

List 4 common Compensation methods:

1. _____

2. _____

3. _____

4. _____

Salary is when you receive a predetermined payment calculated at a/an _____ rate, which is based on minimum wage or a wage set by the salon owner.

$8 WAGE X 40 HOURS = _____ WITHOUT DEDUCTIONS

The percentage of the dollars you brought into the salon from Guest services and products is called _____.

$800 SERVICES PERFORMED @ 50% COMMISSION = _____ WITHOUT DEDUCTIONS

Additional income to your regular pay, given by your Guests for a job well done, that must be reported for tax purposes is called _____. When calculated with regular pay, tips can add a significant amount to your annual income and be beneficial to your credit when applying for loans and other personal items.

$400 REGULAR PAY + $60 TIPS = _____ WEEKLY X 50 WEEKS

= _____ ANNUAL INCOME WITHOUT DEDUCTIONS

# INTERVIEWING

When interviewing, there are many questions you will be asked. You will also be interviewing the potential employer to make sure the salon is the right fit for you.

**List below some of the questions and/or topics you will want to ask or discuss during your interview.**

## WHAT DO YOU WANT TO ASK...

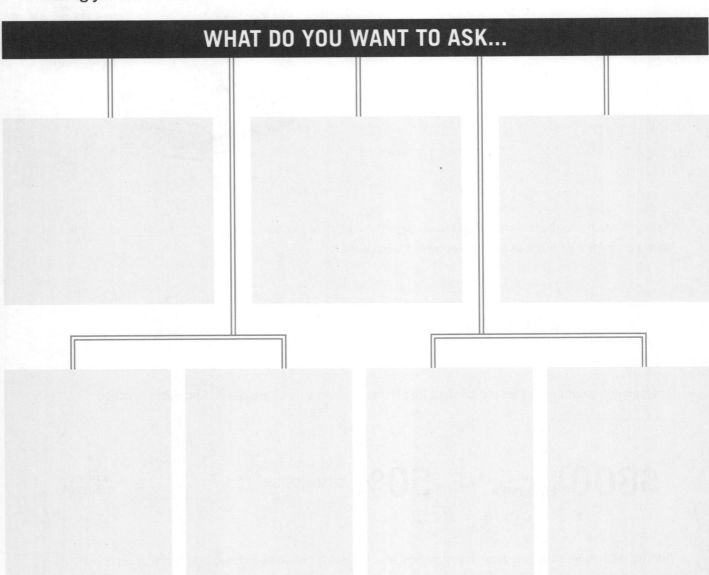

# INTERVIEWING

A document that states all the responsibilities and tasks for the particular position you are applying is called a _____ _____. It may also contain the expectations and standards of the salon.

In the space below, create a job description that you would give to potential employees if you were the salon owner looking to hire a new stylist for your salon.

**Position:**

**Essential Duties:**

**Essential Skills:**

**Physical Requirements:**

**Other:**

# INTERVIEWING

A document that is signed and agreed upon between two parties that predetermines how certain situations will be handled if they arise is called a _____  _____.

In the space below, create a written agreement that you would give to potential employees if you were the salon owner looking to hire a new stylist for your salon.

**Position:**

**Employee and Employer:**

**Date:**

**Specifics:**
      Example – hours, pay, customer list, termination, etc.

# MARKETING INVESTMENT

Several marketing techniques can be used to promote yourself and/or salon for little investment, other than your time. "ROI" is an acronym for _____ _____ _____.
This is the process that you can use to figure the effectiveness of dollars spent on marketing tools. One important piece to the process is the amount your typical Guest spends on products and services per visit, known as _____ _____.

## Determine the following "ROI":

**$45.50** AVERAGE TICKET **X** **10** VISITS PER YEAR **=** $ _____ TOTAL INCOME PER GUEST

You spent $1,500 to market new Guests. Using the total income per Guest, how many new Guests will you need to retain in order to break even on your investment? _____

**Listed below are some of the marketing techniques available to you. How would you utilize them? Be creative, think outside the box, and be professional.**

**WEBSITES**

**EMAIL CAMPAIGNS**

**DIGITAL NEWSLETTERS**

**BLOGGING**

**DIRECT MAIL**

**NEWSPAPER**

**COMMUNITY INVOLVEMENT**

## ACROSS

**1.** supplies used in the daily operation of a salon

**5.** a group of people and/or stockholders investing in a business creates a

**8.** records associated with a business that must be organized and maintained to satisfy all taxing requirements

**10.** all of the team members in a salon that an employer employs

**11.** a business where two or more persons share in the ownership and operation of the business

**12.** a business that is solely owned and managed by one person

## DOWN

**2.** the skills and processes necessary to run a successful salon

**3.** a report or plan of action that describes the current or projected future of a business

**4.** space rented in a salon where a stylist can run their own business performing services; also known as chair rental

**6.** an accounting practice of maintaining and organizing all business records

**7.** a written agreement that once purchased, guarantees the business is protected in the event of an accident, injury, fire, theft and loss of ability to do business

**9.** the money you will invest to start a business

# MY NEED TO KNOW notes:

_____

_____

_____

_____

_____

_____

_____

_____

_____

_____

_____

_____

_____

_____

_____

_____

_____

_____

_____

_____

_____

_____

_____

_____

_____

_____

_____

_____

# SITUATIONAL SCENARIOS

**1.** Mary arrives at the salon for her scheduled appointment and checks in. The receptionist nods her head and turns to another Guest. Mary goes to the reception area to have a seat. What should the receptionist have done for Mary?

    **a)** Have another stylist greet her
    **b)** Verbally greet and show Mary to the reception area
    **c)** Gone to the food court
    **d)** Introduced her to other Guests

**2.** To avoid any miscommunication with your Guests regarding appointment times and/or the service(s) scheduled for their next appointment, what is the best practice?

    **a)** Mail a reminder card
    **b)** Send a text message
    **c)** Call your Guests a day or two prior to their scheduled appointment and confirm the time and service(s)
    **d)** All of the above

**3.** You have been working toward a pay increase. You have a performance review scheduled with your salon manager. What will you want to ask your salon manager?

    **a)** To cut back your hours
    **b)** When will you be able to get a part-time assistant
    **c)** How many other stylists are they meeting with
    **d)** What are the requirements for receiving a pay increase

**4.** To gain respect from your Guests and display a good sense of integrity, you should:

    **a)** Recommend specific products and services that would be beneficial for your Guest's needs
    **b)** Provide the best shampoo experience in your salon
    **c)** Share personal information about your co-workers with your Guests
    **d)** Both a and b

**5.** In order to increase your current pay without an increase in pricing, you could?

    **a)** Reduce your hours
    **b)** Use marketing tools to increase referrals and request business
    **c)** Work only daytime hours, no evenings or weekends
    **d)** Overcharge your Guests for services you perform

**6.** You are interested in a management position within the salon where you currently work. When meeting with your manager to discuss your options, you should be prepared to hear the following:

    **a)** That your manager has no intention of leaving and the position will never be open
    **b)** Company policy does not allow for promotion from within
    **c)** Areas that you will need to improve upon in order to be promoted
    **d)** That your hours will be reduced

**7.** During a co-worker's vacation, you serviced several of her regular Guests. One of the Guests has requested to rebook with you, instead of your co-worker. How should you handle this situation?

    **a)** Tell the Guest that unfortunately you cannot service them in the future
    **b)** Schedule the appointment and not discuss it any further
    **c)** Tell all your co-workers
    **d)** Meet with your manager to discuss the Guest's request and let your manager handle any situation that may arise

**8.** Janet is very unhappy with the haircut and haircolor you just completed. You did a thorough consultation and felt you understood Janet's requests. How do you proceed?

    **a)** Ask if she would like a drink – soda, water or coffee
    **b)** Calmly and politely talk with Janet and ask her what she does not like about the cut and/or color and offer to fix it
    **c)** Tell Janet this is exactly what she asked for
    **d)** Schedule Janet's next appointment with another stylist

**9.** Your new co-workers, Sue and Barry, are having a personal disagreement. They are trying to get you to take sides. Your best plan of action is to ask for help from?

    **a)** Your spouse
    **b)** Your parents
    **c)** Your salon manager
    **d)** Other salon employees

**10.** During a conversation with your Guest, they ask you about your political views. What do you do?

    **a)** Continue the conversation, giving your preference
    **b)** Ask other Guests and co-workers what they think
    **c)** Get in an argument with your Guest, stating their views are wrong
    **d)** Change the topic of the conversation as quickly as possible

# TIMED SKILL
# practice

| | START TIME | END TIME | GOAL TIME | | | HOW CAN I IMPROVE? |
|---|---|---|---|---|---|---|
| Station Set-Up / Drape for Service | | | 15 | 10 | 5 | |
| **HAIRCUTTING** | | | | | | |
| Haircut – 0° // 45° // 90° // 180° (shear and/or razor) | | | 45 | 40 | 35 | |
| Tapered Clipper Haircut | | | 50 | 45 | 40 | |
| Combination Haircut (shear and/or razor) | | | 50 | 45 | 40 | |
| Round Brush Blowdry Style | | | 25 | 20 | 15 | |
| Blowdry and Style with Thermal Tools | | | 40 | 35 | 30 | |
| **DESIGN PRINCIPLES** | | | | | | |
| Roller or Curling Iron Set – Basic | | | 35 | 30 | 20 | |
| Pincurl Set (full head) | | | 45 | 40 | 35 | |
| Design Wrap | | | 30 | 25 | 20 | |
| Fingerwaves or Pushwaves (full head) | | | 45 | 40 | 35 | |
| 3-Strand Braid // Vertical Twist Roll | | | 30 | 25 | 20 | |
| Blowdry Style (choice of brushes, tools and fixatives) | | | 25 | 20 | 15 | |
| **HAIRCOLORING** | | | | | | |
| Virgin Application | | | 45 | 40 | 35 | |
| Haircolor Retouch (new growth only) | | | 25 | 20 | 15 | |
| Haircolor Retouch with Color Balancing | | | 45 | 40 | 35 | |
| Partial Foil (weave and slice techniques) | | | 45 | 40 | 35 | |
| Full Head Foil (weave and slice techniques) | | | 80 | 70 | 60 | |
| Lightener Retouch | | | 40 | 35 | 30 | |
| **CHEMICAL TEXTURIZING** | | | | | | |
| Relaxer Retouch | | | 25 | 20 | 15 | |
| Virgin Relaxer Application | | | 45 | 40 | 35 | |
| Keratin Straightening (ironing technique only – full head) | | | 45 | 40 | 35 | |
| 9-Block Sectioning for Perm | | | 20 | 15 | 10 | |
| Basic Perm Wrap (full head) | | | 60 | 55 | 50 | |
| Partial Perm Wrap | | | 35 | 30 | 25 | |
| **NAIL CARE** | | | | | | |
| Basic Manicure (including hand and arm massage) | | | 45 | 40 | 30 | |
| Basic Pedicure (including foot and leg massage) | | | 60 | 50 | 45 | |
| Polish Only – 10 Fingernails (base coat / polish / topcoat) | | | 35 | 25 | 15 | |
| Polish Only – 10 Toenails (base coat / polish / topcoat) | | | 35 | 25 | 15 | |

*Pathway to Success*

# MY NEED TO KNOW notes:

# PATHWAY TO SUCCESS
## STATE BOARD THEORY REVIEW

1. Percentage of total dollars you receive from services and retail products sold is:

   a) retail      b) hourly      c) commission      d) expenses

2. Supplies used in daily salon operations:

   a) stocked      b) inventory      c) consumption      d) management

3. The money a typical Guest spends on services and products during their salon visit determines:

   a) spending ticket      b) retail ticket      c) tip      d) average ticket

4. _____ is using verbal and non-verbal cues to show you are interested in the conversation:

   a) Pretend listening      b) Active listening      c) Partial listening      d) Evaluative listening

5. Certain regulatory agencies and taxing laws require that you maintain correct:

   a) business records      b) Guest records      c) stylist records      d) color records

6. A _____ should include the Guest's name and contact information, along with the original requested time and date of appointment:

   a) request list      b) appointment list      c) stylist list      d) cancellation list

7. A _____ is required when seeking financial assistance to open your salon:

   a) résumé      b) business referral      c) business plan      d) credit plan

8. _____ is when a stylist rents space in an existing establishment and has the ability to independently generate revenue:

   a) Booth rental      b) Salon rental      c) Partnership      d) Corporation

9. An image or trademark that represents you or your business:

   a) a brand      b) networking      c) impression      d) all of the above

10. The movement and position of your body is a communication skill:

   a) active listening      b) body language      c) verbal communication      d) poor attitude

11. Connecting with potential Guests in a social setting is:

a) non-verbal     b) networking     c) retention     d) retailing communication

12. The steps you take to ensure your Guest always leaves with a positive impression:

a) negative impression   b) positive impression   c) organized impression   d) impression management

13. Finding solutions to your Guest's concerns and developing a mental picture of your Guest's expectation is determined during the:

a) greeting     b) consultation     c) service     d) retailing

14. A form of ownership by a group of people that requires the highest level of legal consideration and is organized and designed by a lawyer:

a) individual     b) joint     c) partnership     d) corporation

15. Marketing can include which type of communication:

a) written     b) verbal     c) visual     d) all of the above

16. A policy purchased to protect from risk of loss:

a) taxes     b) lease     c) partnership     d) insurance

17. Gaining new Guests through word-of-mouth recommendation:

a) Guest up-selling     b) Guest rebooking     c) Guest referral     d) Guest retention

18. The moral standards that guide a person's conduct:

a) attitude     b) self-esteem     c) self-worth     d) ethics

19. Scheduling your Guest's next appointment while they are still at your station:

a) soft selling     b) hard sell     c) in-the-chair rebooking     d) consultation rebooking

20. An extremely important skill that will affect your retention, referrals and rebooking is your ability to control impressions and experiences throughout the:

a) Guest stylist cycle     b) Guest maintenance cycle     c) Guest service cycle     d) Guest growth cycle

21. A document the employer provides that gives specific information about a job, including the qualifications or skills needed for the job:

   a) job description     b) job application     c) résumé     d) cover letter

22. To set, monitor, and achieve a personal or organizational desired end-point within a specific time frame:

   a) goal     b) schedule     c) ethics     d) appointment

23. The benefits of Guest retention can include growth of paycheck, job security and:

   a) building marketing promotions     b) developing Guest loyalty     c) lowering average ticket price     d) reducing Guest return

24. Budgeting, employee management, inventory and purchasing are necessary skills in:

   a) stylist performance     b) stylist skills     c) salon operation     d) salon service

25. A document that provides details of your work history, education and qualifications for a position:

   a) job description     b) portfolio     c) résumé     d) cover letter

26. What communication uses body gestures and eye movement to send and receive information:

   a) verbal     b) non-verbal     c) active     d) none of the above

27. Identify the open-ended question:

   a) "Would you like some coffee?"     b) "Is the water temperature too hot?"     c) "Are you getting a manicure?"     d) "Explain your normal hair care routine."

28. Pictures of your best work, awards or certificates displayed professionally in an album or electronic folder:

   a) résumé     b) portfolio     c) profile     d) job description

29. What is a strategy to use so that your Guest returns within a specified time for their next service:

   a) retailing     b) networking     c) rebooking     d) referral

30. What is an arrangement in which two or more parties agree to share all costs, profits, and responsibilities of a business:

   a) individual     b) booth rental     c) partnership     d) corporation ownership

31. Showering, brushing your teeth and shampooing your hair are all examples of personal:

a) growth  b) esteem  c) hygiene  d) ethics

32. Being respectful of others, ethical and honorable are traits of:

a) professionalism  b) impression  c) communication  d) assertiveness management

33. Individuals hired and compensated by a company to provide services:

a) personnel  b) Guests  c) customers  d) all of the above

34. An organized system to track all business transactions and expenses:

a) business operation  b) salon operation  c) record keeping  d) record communication

35. Describing your recommendations in a clear, detailed way so that your Guest understands your vision is a form of:

a) verbal communication  b) non-verbal communication  c) body language  d) none of the above

36. An agreement between you and an employer that states that if you decide to leave the salon, you will not work in another salon within a particular mile radius:

a) verbal  b) text  c) single  d) written

37. Shampoo and conditioner your Guest purchases to maintain their style at-home:

a) service supplies  b) retail supplies  c) janitorial supplies  d) manufacturer supplies

38. Your personal assessment of self-worth is your:

a) verbal communication  b) non-verbal communication  c) stress  d) self-esteem

39. Marketing to your desired demographic:

a) awareness market  b) value market  c) appreciation market  d) target-market

40. Recommending that your Guest adds some highlights and/or lowlights to their existing haircolor, is known as:

a) average ticket  b) up-selling  c) Guest referral  d) Guest request

41. All people in the cosmetology field wear bright, vibrant haircolor. This is an example of a/an:

   **a)** fact      **b)** reality      **c)** stereotype      **d)** experiment

42. Keeping and using a cancellation list, and the perception it creates for your Guests, is an example of:

   **a)** appointment service    **b)** value-added service    **c)** irrelevant service    **d)** up-selling service

43. Running late, deadlines, or personal issues can be demanding situations that can cause:

   **a)** relief      **b)** stress      **c)** comfort      **d)** passion

44. An individual who has total responsibility for all profits and losses of a business:

   **a)** sole proprietor    **b)** joint owner    **c)** partner    **d)** corporation

45. Paraphrasing uses your:

   **a)** words to summarize what you heard    **b)** expertise to up-sell a service    **c)** eyes to read your Guest's body language    **d)** hands to perform a service

**My Need To Know Notes:**

_____

_____

_____

_____

_____

_____

_____

_____

_____

_____

_____

_____

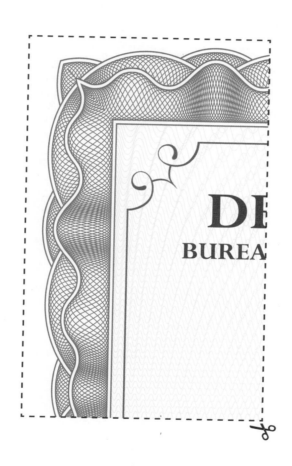

# HAIRCUTTING

# SAFETY AND DISINFECTION

## INFECTION

**What is an Infection?**

The invasion of the body tissues by disease-causing bacteria (pathogenic) or viruses.

**What causes an Infection?**

1. disease-causing bacteria (pathogenic)
2. virus

**Signs of an Infection**

1. H – heat
2. A – Ache
3. R – Redness
4. P – Pus
5. S – Swelling

**Describe the difference between Contamination and Decontamination:**

Contamination: presence of unclean materials/tools on a surface. Decontamination: removal of any infectious materials on tools or surfaces by disinfection guidelines.

**What methods can be used to fight Contamination?**

1. Disinfecting:
2. Sterilization:

**How does Porous or Nonporous affect cleaning and disinfecting?**

_____

_____

**What government regulations or guidelines help to protect against health hazards?**

_____

_____

_____

**Describe Exposure Incident:**

_____

_____

_____

# BLOODBORNE PATHOGEN STANDARD PROCEDURE

# 8 step procedure
*exposure to blood*

1. __Protect__
   // If you are the person who has been cut, __stop__ the service and clean your injured area.
   // If your Guest has been cut, __stop__ the service, put on protective gloves and clean the injured area.

2. __Apply__
   Use __antiseptic__ and/or liquid or spray __styptic__ as appropriate.

3. __Dress__
   _____ the injury with the appropriate dressing.

4. __Cover__
   _____ injured area with finger guard or glove as appropriate.

5. __Clean__
   _____ all tools and work station with EPA-registered disinfectant.

6. __Double__ – __Bag__
   _____ of all contaminated materials in a clearly labeled bag.

7. Fill out an __accident form__ when applicable.

8. __Return__ to service.

CHECK YOUR STATE LAWS AND REGULATORY AGENCIES FOR ANY SPECIFICS REGARDING BLOOD SPILL PROCEDURES.

Haircutting

# DISORDERS AND DISEASES | CROSSWORD PUZZLE

## DOWN

**1.** self-movement

**2.** long, rod-shaped bacteria that cause tetanus, tuberculosis and influenza

**3.** bacteria shaped into chains that grow in curved lines and cause strep throat and blood poisoning

**6.** bacteria that are harmful and cause disease

**8.** the same characteristics as a furuncle, but larger

**9.** circular-shaped bacteria

**10.** bacterial invasion of the body that disrupts normal function of health

**12.** an ailment or illness that disrupts a normal function of health

**13.** boil or abscess of the skin located in the hair follicle

**14.** spiral-shaped bacteria that cause syphilis and lyme disease

## ACROSS

**4.** one-celled microorganisms

**5.** spherical-shaped bacteria that grow in pairs and cause pneumonia

**7.** long appendages that propel bacteria through liquid

**8.** hair-like projections that help bacilli and spirilla to move

**11.** bacteria that are not harmful

**14.** bacteria that grow in clusters and infect the skin and/or scalp

**15.** infections or diseases that can be transferred from one person to another by contact

**16.** pathogenic bacteria that live on or inside another organism

**17.** infectious pathogenic microorganisms that are present in human blood and can cause disease

# HAIR STRUCTURE

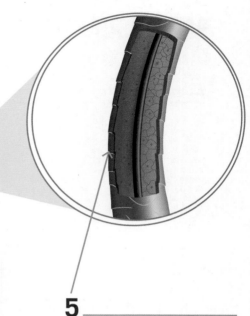

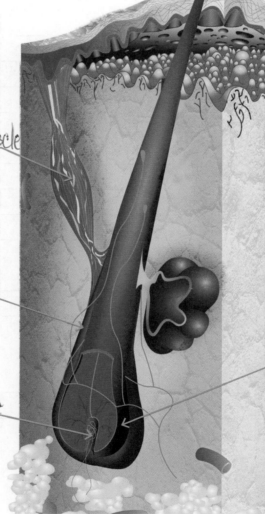

**5** _____

**1** Arrector Pili Muscle

**2** Hair Follicle

**3** Dermal Papilla

Hair Bulb **4**

- Arrector Pili
- Cuticle
- Dermal Papilla
- Hair Follicle
- Hair Bulb

# STAGES OF HAIR GROWTH

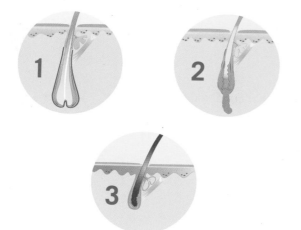

1. ___Anagen___ period of active growth

2. ___Catagen___ period of breakdown and change

3. ___Telogen___ period of rest

---

# STAGES OF HAIR GROWTH | CROSSWORD PUZZLE

## DOWN

**2.** the study of hair, disorders, diseases and hair care

**3.** pigmented hair on the scalp, arms, legs and in the nose and ears

**5.** soft, white, downy hair commonly found on newborn babies

## ACROSS

**1.** process by which newly formed cells in the hair bulb mature

**4.** all hair goes through how many stages of growth

**6.** strong, fibrous protein derived from amino acids that make up hair and nails

# DISORDERS OF THE SCALP AND HAIR | WORD SEARCH

1. _Alopecia_ — hair loss in abnormal amounts

2. _Alopecia Areata_ — patches of hair loss

3. _Alopecia Totalis_ — balding on the entire head

4. _Alopecia Universalis_ — balding over the entire body

5. _Androgenic Alopecia_ — male or female pattern baldness

6. _Fallen Hair_ — is naturally shed

7. _Fragilitas Crinium_ — brittle hair

8. _Monilethrix_ — beaded hair

9. _Pityriasis_ — commonly known as dandruff

10. _Pityriasis Steatoides_ — also known as Seborrheic Dermatitis

11. _Postpartum Alopecia_ — period of temporary hair loss after childbirth

12. _Telogen Effluvium_ — hair is prematurely pushed into the telogen stage

13. _Traction Alopecia_ — hair loss due to excessive pulling or stretching of the hair

14. _Trichoptilosis_ — split ends

15. _Trichorrehexis Nodosa_ — knotted hair

```
S  T  R  I  C  H  O  R  R  E  H  E  X  I  S  N  O  D  O  S  A  D
P  I  Q  R  P  O  S  T  P  A  R  T  U  M  A  L  O  P  E  C  I  A
F  L  L  A  L  O  P  E  C  I  A  T  O  T  A  L  I  S  V  K  L  B
L  A  F  A  W  M  K  G  T  K  H  C  K  J  T  N  P  B  N  W  A  Q
H  P  N  W  S  R  G  L  Z  X  R  F  N  R  V  L  T  F  N  T  F  T
X  T  B  D  N  R  V  F  Z  R  T  F  I  T  W  Z  R  G  A  J  A  R
I  C  E  F  R  R  E  R  X  K  G  C  D  X  D  A  Y  E  Y  G  L  A
R  K  T  L  K  O  T  V  M  G  H  Y  N  G  G  L  R  D  L  V  L  C
H  Y  Q  D  O  V  G  Z  I  O  R  S  T  I  L  A  M  T  K  A  E  T
T  T  P  T  X  G  T  E  P  N  I  T  L  F  A  F  J  K  Z  I  N  I
E  M  Z  T  F  Q  E  T  N  S  U  I  W  I  R  D  G  B  F  C  H  O
L  X  D  Q  R  Q  I  N  A  I  T  A  C  H  L  H  K  T  R  E  A  N
I  G  B  M  M  L  G  I  E  A  C  E  I  T  F  V  P  M  L  P  I  A
N  B  M  Q  O  P  R  Q  S  F  P  A  J  C  N  K  G  K  P  O  R  L
O  T  M  S  B  Y  B  C  T  O  F  C  L  J  E  K  X  M  F  L  Z  O
M  V  I  X  T  T  R  Q  L  N  Q  L  L  O  R  P  M  R  P  A  K  P
B  S  F  I  T  I  Z  A  D  K  K  R  U  K  P  Q  O  M  H  F  F  E
G  K  P  K  N  L  M  M  W  L  G  L  D  V  B  E  F  L  C  C  N  C
L  T  Q  I  Z  Z  N  P  Z  K  Y  H  K  P  I  L  C  Y  A  W  F  I
T  B  U  K  T  T  P  Y  H  R  Q  N  X  L  Y  U  L  I  C  M  W  A
G  M  X  P  V  D  J  L  L  M  M  F  F  L  T  D  M  K  A  M  R  T
N  P  I  T  Y  R  I  A  S  I  S  S  T  E  A  T  O  I  D  E  S  J
```

# DISEASES OF THE SCALP AND HAIR

*Pg. 166*

1. A condition caused by an animal parasite called the head louse is:

   a) Tinea    (b) Pediculosis Capitis    c) Mildew    d) Alopecia

2. A contagious disease caused by a fungal parasite called dermatophyte, also known as Ringworm, is:

   a) Fungi    b) Hirsuties    c) Terminal Hair    (d) Tinea

3. A member of a large group of organisms that include microorganisms, such as yeasts, molds and mildews. Some common scalp and hair diseases are caused by this:

   a) Virus    (b) Fungi    c) Ringworm    d) Beau's Line

4. A fungal infection characterized by a pink scalp with thick, whitish-yellow crusts known as scutula, and also known as Honeycomb Ringworm, is:

   (a) Tinea Favosa    b) Mildew    c) Syphilis    d) Tinea Pedis

5. A condition caused by the microscopic mite called sarcoptes scabei, and also known as the itch mite, is:

   a) Fungi    b) Tinea    (c) Scabies    d) Systemic

6. A fungal infection of the scalp that is caused when fungus attacks the opening of the follicle, making the scalp slightly pink with red spots and a white, scaly appearance is:

   a) Tinea    b) Fragilitas Crinium    c) Pityriasis    (d) Tinea Capitis

7. A superficial fungal infection that commonly affects the skin and is also known as Barber's Itch:

   (a) Tinea Barbae    b) Tinea Favosa    c) Mildew    d) Scabies

# DISORDERS AND DISEASES OF THE SCALP

**Fill in the identifying characteristics and examples for each disorder.**

| DISORDERS OF THE SCALP | CHARACTERISTICS | EXAMPLE | SERVICE |
|---|---|---|---|
| Pityriasis | build-up of white, flaky skin that is shed from the skin/scalp. | dandruff | |
| Pityriasis Steatoides | large, yellow, bran-like flakes | | ✚ |
| Alopecia | | | |
| Alopecia Areata | | | ✚ |
| Alopecia Totalis | | | ✚ |
| Alopecia Universalis | | | ✚ |
| Androgenic Alopecia | | | ✚ |
| Telogen Effluvium | | | ✚ |
| Postpartum Alopecia | | | |
| Traction Alopecia | | | |

| DISORDERS OF THE HAIR | CHARACTERISTICS | EXAMPLE | SERVICE |
|---|---|---|---|
| Fragilitas Crinium | | | |
| Hypertrichosis | | | |
| Monilethrix | | | |
| Trichoptilosis | | | |
| Trichorrhexis Nodosa | | | |

| DISORDERS OF THE SCALP AND HAIR | CHARACTERISTICS | EXAMPLE | SERVICE |
|---|---|---|---|
| Pediculosis Capitis | | | ✚ |
| Scabies | | | ✚ |
| Tinea | | | ✚ |
| Tinea Capitis | | | ✚ |
| Tinea Favosa | | | ✚ |

| DISORDERS OF THE FOLLICLE | CHARACTERISTICS | EXAMPLE | SERVICE |
|---|---|---|---|
| Furuncle | | | ✚ |
| Carbuncle | | | ✚ |

 *Recommend your Guest see a Medical Professional*

Haircutting

# BONES OF THE HEAD

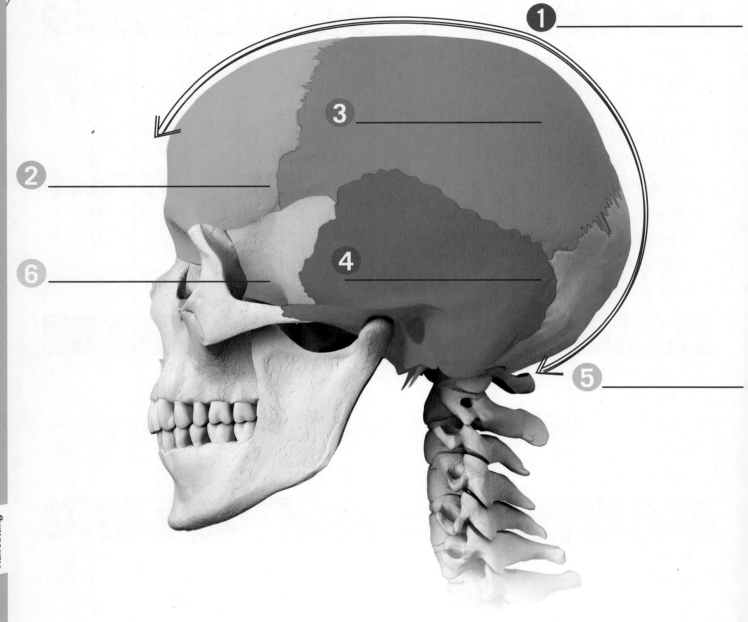

1 _____

3 _____

2 _____

6 _____

4 _____

5 _____

1. covers the top and sides of the head and face

2. bone that forms the forehead

3. consists of 2 bones that form the entire crown

4. consists of 2 bones that form the lower side of the head below the occipital

5. bone that covers the back of the head and sits directly above the nape

6. joins all the bones of the cranium

# BONES OF THE NECK, CHEST AND UPPER BACK

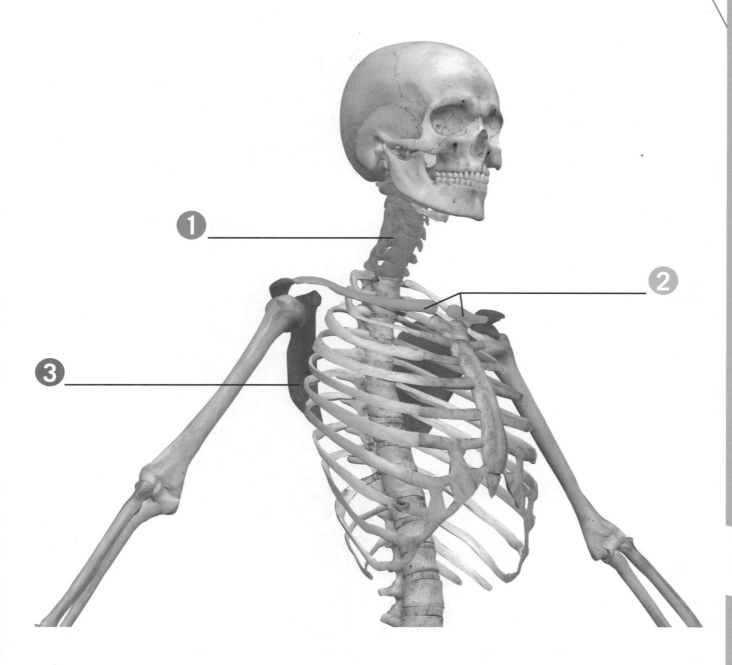

1

2

3

1. consists of 7 vertebrae located in the neck

2. also known as the collar bone

3. consists of 2 large, flat bones that form the back part of the shoulder blades

# MUSCLES OF THE HEAD AND NECK

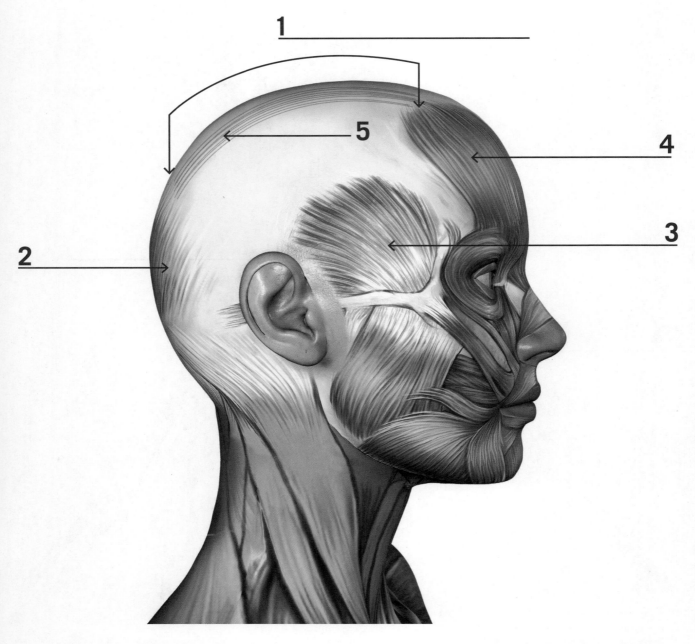

1. this muscle covers the epicranium and is also known as occipito-frontalis

2. this muscle pulls the scalp back

3. this muscle helps in opening and closing the mouth, as in chewing

4. this muscle lifts the eyebrows and pulls the forehead forward, causing wrinkles

5. the tendon that connects the occipitalis and frontalis to form the epicranius

# MUSCLES OF THE UPPER CHEST AND UPPER BACK

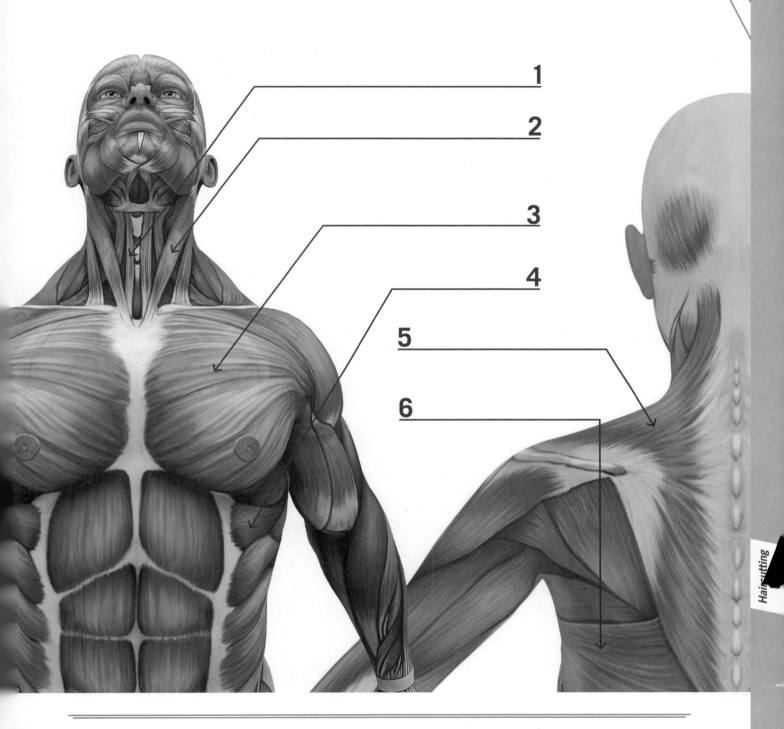

1

2

3

4

5

6

**1.** this muscle moves the lower jaw down, expressing sadness

**2.** this muscle moves the head up and down or side to side

**3.** major muscle that stretches across the front of the upper chest, enabling the arms to swing

**4.** muscle that assists in elevating the arm and in breathing

**5.** this muscle moves the head back and forth and swings the arms

**6.** this muscle helps to extend the arm away from the body and rotate the shoulder

## MATCHING

A. Sternocleidomastoideus

B. Arrector Pili Muscle

C. Epicranial Aponeurosis

D. Trapezius

E. Epicranius / Occipito-frontalis

F. Occipitalis

G. Platysma

H. Temporalis

I. Frontalis

1. _____ the muscle that extends from the tip of the chin to the shoulder and lowers the jaw and lip

2. _____ a muscle of the neck that lowers and rotates the head

3. _____ the muscle that extends from the forehead to the top of the skull

4. _____ the temple muscle located above and in front of the ear that creates the chewing motion of the jaw

5. _____ the flat, triangular muscles that run from the upper back to the back of the neck

6. _____ a small, involuntary muscle located within the skin responsible for 'goose bumps'

7. _____ the broad muscle formed by the joining of the frontalis and occipitalis

8. _____ a tendon that connects the occipitalis and the frontalis

9. _____ the muscle located in the nape of the neck that draws the scalp backward

# WATER WORKS

List the characteristics and the role that each play in hair care.

**Soft Water:**

_____
_____
_____
_____
_____

**Lipophilic:**

_____
_____
_____
_____
_____

**What is a Surfactant and how does it work with water?**

_____
_____
_____
_____
_____

**Hydrophilic:**

_____
_____
_____
_____
_____

**Hard Water:**

_____
_____
_____
_____
_____

# FACE SHAPES

**Label each face shape, then sketch a complementary haircut for each.**

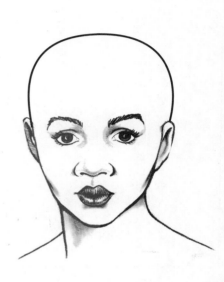

2. _____

1. _____

3. _____

**OVAL SHAPE**

The ideal face shape to be achieved, utilizing various techniques (haircut, haircolor, makeup and styling)

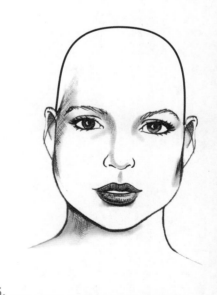

4. _Round_____

6. _____

5. _____

# MY NEED TO KNOW notes:

# SECTIONS AND PARTINGS

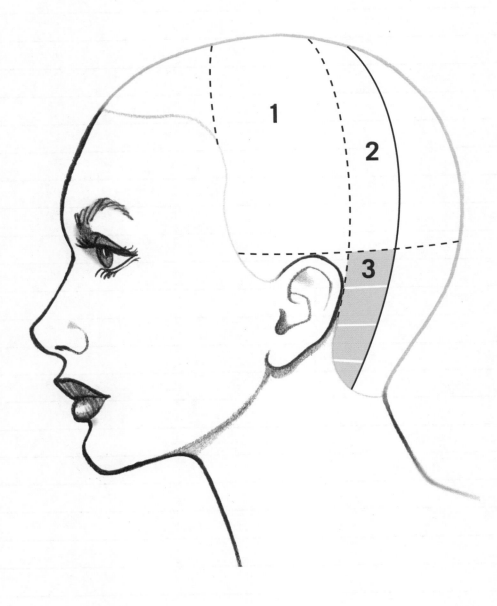

1. areas of the head that allow for control during a haircut _____

2. smaller areas within the main section _____

3. smaller areas within each subsection to separate the hair for better control and more precise haircuts _____

# ESSENTIAL REFERENCE POINTS FOR HAIRCUTTING

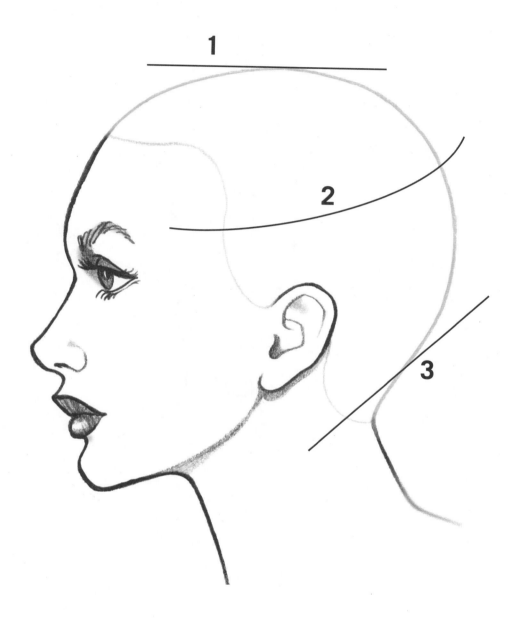

1. highest point of the head

2. largest curve of the head

3. starts at the curved portion of the head, and is located at the base of the head

# REFERENCE POINTS
# FOR HAIRCUTTING

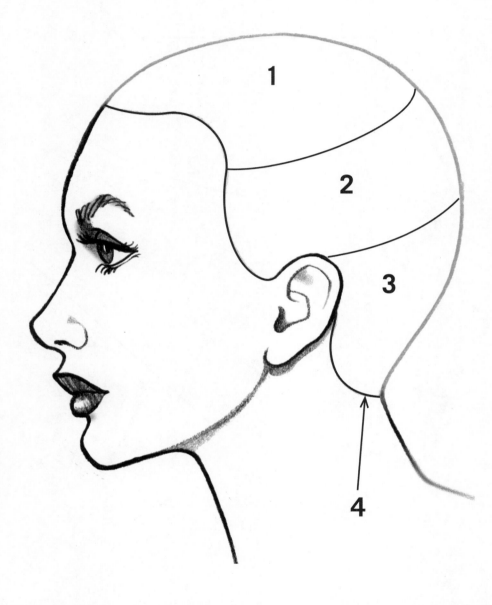

1. _____ inner / internal part of the head

2. _____ outer / external part of the head

3. _____ section of the head from the occipital bone to the hairline

4. _____ the hair that grows around the outermost edge of the face, around ears, and back of the head

# REFERENCE POINTS
# FOR HAIRCUTTING

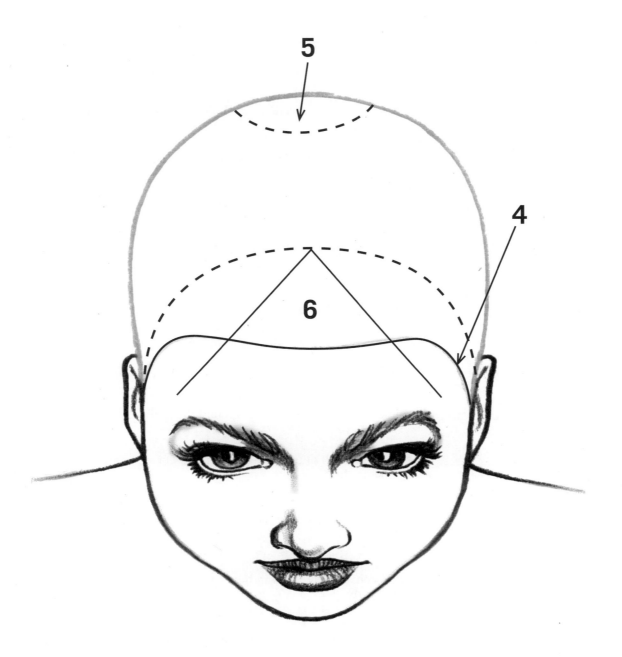

---

4. _____ the hair that grows around the outermost edge of the face, around ears, and back of head

5. _____ area of the head between the apex and parietal ridge; upper back of head

6. _____ front area that can range from the outer corner of the eyes to the apex

# LINES AND ANGLES | WORD SEARCH

1. _____ combinations of straight lines joined together, producing various effects

2. _____ slanting lines that run between horizontal and vertical lines

3. _____ independent lines that normally do not blend

4. _____ degree or angle at which the hair is lifted and combed in relation to the head

5. _____ first section of hair to be cut that determines the length for the rest of the haircut

6. _____ lines that run parallel to the floor

7. _____ this guide is inside a haircut, not around the perimeter

8. _____ the edge or division of a shape; straight and curved are the two basics used in haircutting

9. _____ this distribution is the direction in which the hair moves or falls on the head

10. _____ lines that consistently travel in the same direction at an equal distance apart

11. _____ this distribution is created by directing the hair out of its natural fall

12. _____ fixed or non-moving guide

13. _____ guide that moves or passes from one section to another

14. _____ lines that extend straight up from the floor

15. _____ concentration of hair within an area that can give the appearance of heaviness and density

```
D  N  L  N  P  L  W  H  D  Z  S  R  P  M  C  K
P  V  E  T  H  B  X  N  R  G  H  K  R  J  G  F
X  A  L  L  S  L  K  M  L  R  I  N  O  K  N  G
C  J  R  E  E  K  T  A  N  B  F  G  I  L  I  W
X  R  N  A  Y  V  N  W  L  P  T  S  R  R  L  M
T  I  T  K  L  O  A  A  Z  Y  E  E  E  T  E  Q
L  N  G  R  G  L  C  T  X  N  D  L  T  Y  V  M
C  R  N  A  J  I  E  N  I  Y  C  G  N  T  A  G
C  H  I  R  T  X  K  L  Y  O  T  N  I  H  R  U
D  D  L  R  W  H  N  Q  K  P  N  A  N  R  T  I
M  V  E  K  D  I  S  C  O  N  N  E  C  T  E  D
R  V  Q  J  N  D  H  T  P  H  G  W  V  L  K  E
R  N  D  N  A  T  U  R  A  L  D  F  V  R  L  L
M  Y  R  A  N  O  I  T  A  T  S  P  N  Y  B  I
Y  C  J  R  N  W  E  I  G  H  T  L  I  N  E  N
L  G  L  H  Q  L  A  T  N  O  Z  I  R  O  H  E
```

# GROWTH PATTERNS AND TEXTURE | CROSSWORD PUZZLE

## ACROSS

**2.** hair that grows in a circular growth pattern

**4.** a tuft of hair that stands up and grows in a different direction from the rest of the hair

**5.** hair that has a small diameter or width and feels thin

**8.** the direction the hair grows from the scalp

**10.** hair that has an average diameter or width and thickness

**11.** there are how many types of different hair textures

## DOWN

**1.** the thickness or width of a single strand

**3.** also known as a natural part

**6.** the number of hair strands per square inch on the scalp

**7.** hair that has a large diameter or width and feels thick

**9.** the diameter or width of a single hair strand

# COMBS AND BRUSHES | Identify each tool below, and describe what each is used for.

_____

Uses: _____

_____

Uses: _____

_____

Uses: _____

_____

Uses: _____

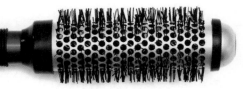

_____

Uses: _____

_____

Uses: _____

_____

Uses: _____

# HAIRCUTTING TOOLS

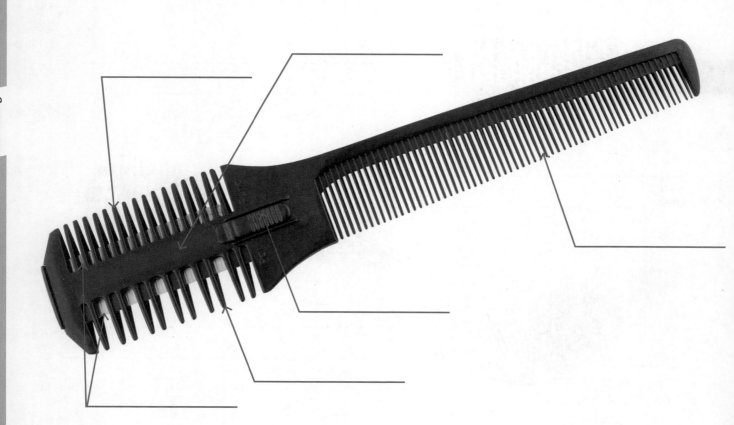

# HAIRCUTTING TOOLS | Label each of the following:

# HAIRCUTTING ELEVATIONS

Label each line with the correct elevation.

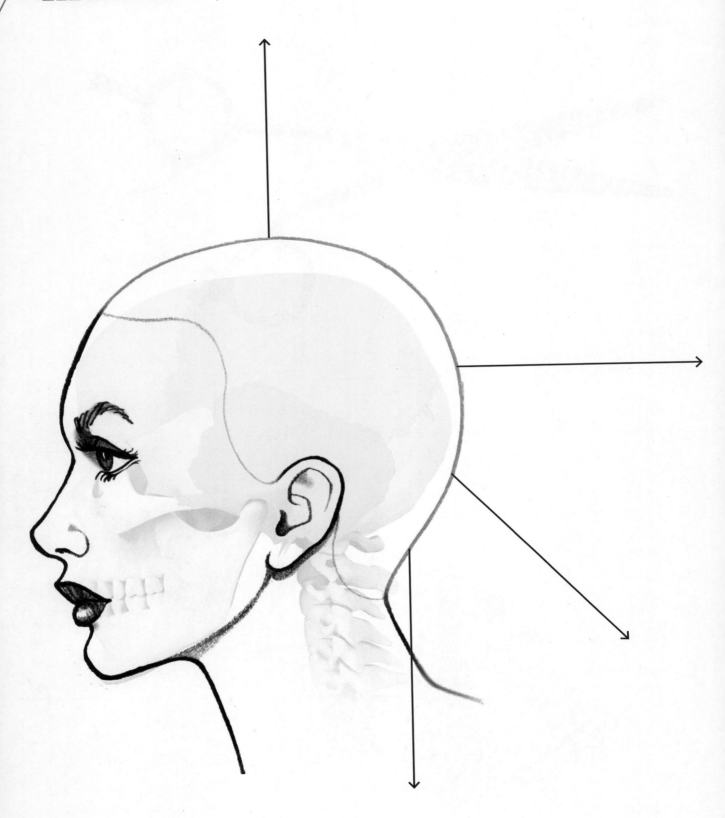

# HAIRCUTTING FUNDAMENTALS

Pictured below are the 4 fundamental haircutting elevations to all haircuts. List the other 'also known as' names associated with each cutting elevation.

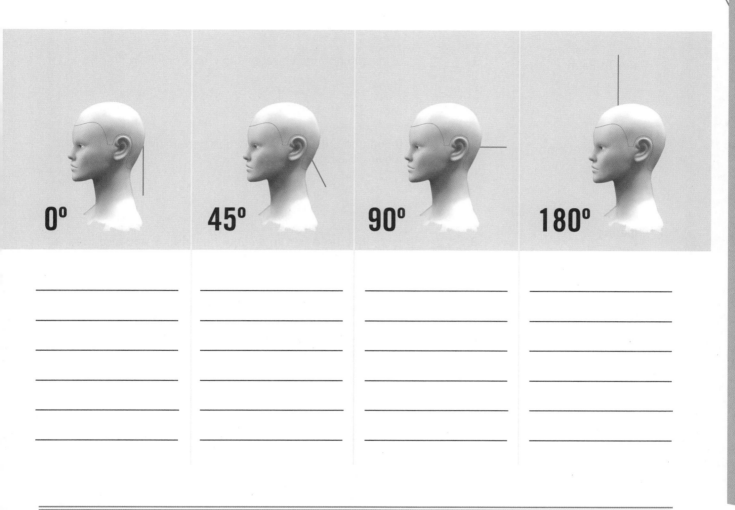

0°   45°   90°   180°

| 0° | 45° | 90° | 180° |
|---|---|---|---|
| _____ | _____ | _____ | _____ |
| _____ | _____ | _____ | _____ |
| _____ | _____ | _____ | _____ |
| _____ | _____ | _____ | _____ |
| _____ | _____ | _____ | _____ |
| _____ | _____ | _____ | _____ |

## How can each of the following influence a haircut?

**1.** Guest head position: _____

**2.** shear and finger position: _____

**3.** hair texture: _____

**4.** tension: _____

**5.** shrinkage: _____

**6.** cross-checking: _____

## MATCHING

A. **Palm-To-Palm**

B. **Clipper-Over-Comb**

C. **Tapering**

D. **Shear-Over-Comb**

E. **Flat Top Haircut**

F. **Razor Rotation**

G. **Combination Haircut**

H. **Edging**

1. _____ using two or more elevations to create one haircut

2. _____ technique utilizing small circular movements, continuously moving the razor and comb

3. _____ technique used to trim around the hairline; and also used to create a clean line or design within a haircut

4. _____ haircutting technique that positions the palms of your hands facing each other

5. _____ technique used to blend weight lines using a clipper and comb

6. _____ haircutting technique where the hair at the perimeter is very close and gradually gets longer as it progresses up the head

7. _____ technique used to blend weight lines using shears and a comb

8. _____ forms into a square shape on the top of the head

# TEXTURIZING TOOLS AND TECHNIQUES

What is Texturizing and why would you use it? _____

_____

_____

_____

**In your own words, define each of the texturizing techniques and what haircutting tool(s) can be used to create the desired effect.**

**1.** Beveling _____

**2.** Point Cutting _____

**3.** Carving _____

**4.** Notching _____

**5.** Slithering _____

**6.** Chunking _____

# DEVELOPING YOUR HAIRCUTTING COMMUNICATION AND SOLUTION SKILLS

What consultation question(s) will you have prepared to ask your Guest?

_____

_____

_____

_____

Your Guest states that they were having problems styling their previous haircut. How would you respond?

_____

_____

_____

Your Guest expresses they would like to cut their hair (which is reaching to the middle of their back) above their shoulders. What recommendations would you give?

_____

_____

_____

Your Guest has one length, overly thick, wavy hair and wants to get a layered, above-the-shoulders length haircut. What suggestions could you offer to your Guest?

_____

_____

_____

Haircutting

## SERVICE RECOMMENDATIONS

What styling recommendations will you discuss with your Guest and why?

_____

_____

_____

## MAINTENANCE RECOMMENDATIONS

When discussing a maintenance routine with your Guest, how often will you suggest they rebook?

_____

_____

_____

## PRODUCT RECOMMENDATIONS

What product recommendations will you discuss with your Guest and why?

_____

_____

_____

Shampoo:_____

Conditioner:_____

Styling:_____

Finishing:_____

# WELL-BODY, WELL-BEING

Define **Ergonomics:**

_____

_____

_____

How do the tools you use, the position of your body, and the shoes you wear affect your well-being?

_____

_____

_____

What can you do to ensure your personal comfort and ensure the longevity of your career?

_____

_____

_____

What can you do to ensure the comfort and safety of your Guests?

_____

_____

_____

# WORKSHOP
# standards

## Safety and Infection Control:

Disinfect work station *(before and after each service)*
Set up work station with required, clean service tools

## Consultation:

Scalp Analysis:  ☐oily  ☐normal  ☐dry  ☐abrasions
Hair Analysis:  ☐density  ☐texture  ☐elasticity  ☐porosity
Drape: neck strip, towel, cape, towel

## Shampoo Bowl Safety:

Maintain control of nozzle at all times, with constant temperature check
Appropriate amount of product is dispensed
Rinse product(s) thoroughly from scalp and hair
Disinfect shampoo bowl and water nozzle

## Haircutting Techniques: *Shear and Razor*

Neatly section and clip hair into 4 quadrants
Maintain clean partings and subsections throughout haircut
Proper elevation and tension for:  ☐0°  ☐45°  ☐90°  ☐180°
Comb and shears properly held throughout service
Cross-check for accuracy
Proper blending techniques using one or more of the following tools:
☐Shear-Over-Comb  ☐Clipper-Over-Comb  ☐Razor
Appropriate edging and clean up around ears, neckline, sideburns

## Haircutting Techniques: *Clipper*

Proper control and use of clipper
Proper use of clipper attachments
Proper blending techniques using one or more of the following tools:
☐Shear-Over-Comb  ☐Clipper-Over-Comb  ☐Razor  ☐Clipper-Guard-Attachments
Appropriate edging and clean up around ears, neckline, sideburns

## Finishing of Service:

Apply appropriate amount and type of fixative(s) to damp / wet hair
Dry hair 80% before using styling brushes
Maintain proper control and temperature of all electrical tools
Complete style as desired
Recommend at-home maintenance product(s)

Haircutting

# SITUATIONAL SCENARIOS

**1.** What tools must be readily available at your station if your day is fully booked with back-to-back haircut appointments?

    **a)** Wet disinfectant, cutting combs, haircolor bowl / brush, foils, shears, blowdryer
    **b)** Cape, towels, wet disinfectant, brushes, gloves, water bottle
    **c)** Cape, towels, neck strips, water bottle, clips, shears, combs, brushes, razor, blowdryer, wet disinfectant
    **d)** Wet disinfectant, tail comb, end papers, foils, brushes, flat iron, trimmer

**2.** Betty, your request Guest, arrives 20 minutes late for her 45 minute appointment for a new haircut and style. That leaves you only 25 minutes to complete the service before your next Guest, a hair removal service arrives. Which of the following scenarios is the best way to handle this situation?

    **a)** Tell Betty she is late, and she has to reschedule her appointment
    **b)** Greet Betty and politely let her know her appointment was at 3:00 pm and you cannot do her haircut today because you have a 3:45 pm appointment
    **c)** Tell Betty another stylist will have to do her service today
    **d)** Politely greet Betty and let her know her appointment was at 3:00 pm, and you have a 3:45 pm request Guest appointment for facial waxing. However, you would be able to start her haircut, stop to service your 3:45 pm Guest, then finish after that Guest

**3.** John wants excessive bulk removed from his hair. What technique would you use to achieve this?

    **a)** Notching – 226
    **b)** Slithering – 227
    **c)** Beveling – 227
    **d)** Thinning – 225

**4.** Jennifer, a first time Guest, has long, natural ringlet-curled hair that reaches her waist. She is requesting that you cut it so it falls to her shoulders. To achieve the desired length, how should you cut Jennifer's hair?

    **a)** Section and cut Jennifer's hair right at her shoulders
    **b)** Recommend to Jennifer that she not go that short
    **c)** Section and cut the guideline at least two inches below Jennifer's shoulders
    **d)** Recommend adding layers and begin cutting right at Jennifer's shoulders

**5.** Arriving late for work, you notice that you have missed your first appointment. Your Guest arrived on time, waited, but had to leave. You should do which of the following?

    **a)** Set up your station and greet your next Guest
    **b)** Greet your next Guest, and let them know you will be with them in 5 minutes. Then call your first Guest, apologize and reschedule their appointment, offering them a discount or complimentary service for their inconvenience
    **c)** Wait for the first Guest to call back and reschedule
    **d)** Call your first Guest and say that they must have scheduled their appointment after you left the previous day, because you did not know you had an appointment

Haircutting

**6.** Jane would like her hair to be all _one length_. To keep the haircut ⌐uniform,⌐ be sure to always use your initial guideline and what elevation?

    a) 0° - 212
    b) 45° - 214
    c) 90° - 216
    d) 180° - 218

**7.** Your Guest is requesting a new haircut, but wants to keep the _length with no layers._ What do you do? 0°/90°

    a) Tell them that maintaining length is impossible
    b) Explain to your Guest that you can cut their hair, but length will definitely be removed
    c) Get more in depth information as to exactly what they are wanting, by showing them pictures or drawing diagrams, to help ensure you have a clear understanding
    d) Have them reschedule with another stylist

**8.** To achieve a 45° elevation haircut, you should use which bone as a reference point?

    a) Nape
    b) Temporal bone
    c) Crown — 135
    d) Occipital bone

**9.** During the consultation with your Guest, you notice unusual growth patterns that will make the requested clipper cut challenging. How should you proceed?

    a) Explain to your Guest that they have many cowlicks and whorls. Special cutting techniques will be used and caution will be taken when doing the cut
    b) Begin the cut and leave the challenging areas untouched
    c) Explain to your Guest that you are unskilled in using the clipper for such a challenging haircut
    d) Consult with your Guest and recommend a different, longer haircut

**10.** Maria is normally seen with her hair pulled back in a tight ponytail and/or braids. She noticed unusual hair loss before, during and after pregnancy. What type of hair loss is this called?

    a) Inherited alopecia
    b) Alopecia areata
    c) Traction alopecia
    d) Trichoptilosis

# practical PREP

*Each skill will be checked by your Educator and feedback will be provided.*
*Met Skill = 1 point / Not Met Skill = 0 points*

**POINTS**

## Safety and Disinfection:

Disinfects work station *(before and after each service)*

Station set up with required tools

Drapes for haircut service

Performs scalp and hair analysis

Neatly divides and clips hair into 4 quadrants

**Feedback:**

## Haircutting Techniques: *Shears / Razor*

Measures and takes a ½" horizontal parting starting at the nape

Establishes guideline

Removes ½" to 1" of hair at a 0°

Demonstrates proper tension

Demonstrates 45° using proper subsectioning

Demonstrates 90° using proper subsectioning

Demonstrates 180° using proper subsectioning

Properly completes a 45° into a 90° combination cut on a single quadrant

Demonstrates proper blending techniques utilizing shear-over-comb and razor

Handles shears and/or razor safely at all times

**Feedback:**

## Haircutting Techniques: *Clipper*

Demonstrates proper holding position of clipper

Properly attaches clipper guard(s)

Completes tapering technique on a single quadrant

Demonstrates proper blending techniques utilizing clipper-over-comb

Finishes with clean up around ears and hairline

**Feedback:**

# HAIRCUTTING
## STATE BOARD THEORY REVIEW

1. At this elevation, no lifting or raising of the hair is required during the cutting process, producing maximum weight:

   a) 0°          b) 45°          c) 90°          d) 180°

2. This elevation provides graduation and stacking with medium elevation:

   a) 0°          b) 45°          c) 90°          d) 180°

3. This elevation provides uniform lengths:

   a) 0°          b) 45°          c) 90°          d) 180°

4. At this elevation, lengths become progressively longer starting from the top to the bottom:

   a) 0°          b) 45°          c) 90°          d) 180°

5. A reaction to a product is referred to as the following:

   a) alopecia          b) trichoptilosis          c) monilethrix          d) an allergy

6. Abnormal amount of hair loss:

   a) pityriasis          b) trichoptilosis          c) alopecia          d) trichorrehexis nodosa

7. An area on the scalp that is smooth, slightly pink, irregularly shaped and lacking hair:

   a) alopecia areata     b) androgenic alopecia     c) pityriasis steatoides     d) fragilitas crinium

8. An extreme case where an autoimmune disease attacks hair follicles over the entire head:

   a) alopecia totalis     b) alopecia universalis     c) androgenic alopecia     d) traction alopecia

9. _____ is a medical condition involving loss of all hair over the entire body:

   a) Alopecia areata     b) Alopecia universalis     c) Androgenic alopecia     d) Traction alopecia

10. The active growth phase of the hair follicles:

   a) anagen          b) catagen          c) keratin          d) telogen

11. Androgenic alopecia affects the following:

   a) male          b) female          c) both a and b          d) none of the above

# HAIRCUTTING
## STATE BOARD THEORY REVIEW

12. The space formed when two straight lines connect:

a) angle     b) length     c) form     d) balance

13. A detergent-based shampoo that offers deep cleansing abilities, is easily rinsed from hair, and is less expensive:

a) color treated     b) curl reducing     c) anionic     d) cationic

14. In order to eliminate the growth of microorganisms while preventing and/or reducing infection, _____ should be used directly on the skin:

a) rubbing alcohol     b) disinfectant     c) antiseptic     d) peroxide

15. This long rod-shaped bacteria causes tetanus, tuberculosis and influenza:

a) cocci     b) bacilli     c) spirilla     d) none of the above

16. This portion of the head is located by placing a comb flat on top of the head:

a) interior     b) exterior     c) apex     d) occipital

17. Contraction of this muscle causes hairs to stand on end:

a) epicranius     b) arrector pili     c) frontalis     d) aponeurosis

18. Pathogenic and non-pathogenic are two types of:

a) micros     b) bacteria     c) germs     d) all of the above

19. A finished look that is well balanced is equal in:

a) size     b) weight     c) both size and weight     d) proportion

20. A skin disease that is created from a superficial fungal infection:

a) tinea     b) tinea barbae     c) scabies     d) pediculosis capitis

21. A haircutting technique that influences the movement of the hair to naturally turn under:

a) beveling     b) cutting     c) shaving     d) thinning

22. _____ developed a bloodborne pathogen standard to protect licensed professionals from health hazards caused by exposure incidents and other potentially infectious materials in the salon:

   a) OSHA          b) EPA          c) PPE          d) SDS

23. _____ is the resting stage of hair growth:

   a) Anagen        b) Catagen      c) Keratin      d) Telogen

24. During hair growth the break down phase is known as:

   a) anagen        b) catagen      c) keratin      d) telogen

25. In haircutting, a carving technique uses shears that are _____ while moving through the hair:

   a) opened        b) partially opened and closed      c) closed      d) none of the above

26. A surfactant that removes dirt from the hair so that it feels soft:

   a) cationic      b) ionic        c) anionic      d) none of the above

27. The neck, where the spinal column begins, consists of _____ cervical vertebrae:

   a) 5             b) 10           c) 7            d) 15

28. Haircutting technique that is known as weave cutting is:

   a) channeling    b) beveling     c) texturizing  d) slithering

29. A texturizing technique that removes larger sections of hair:

   a) notch cutting b) slithering   c) chunking     d) beveling

30. The circular-shaped bacteria that produces strep throat:

   a) cocci         b) bacilli      c) spirilla     d) flagella

31. A haircut consisting of 45° and 90° elevations is considered to be a:

   a) stacked haircut   b) solid haircut   c) combination haircut   d) texturizing technique

32. The disinfectant must remain _____ on the surface to have proper contact time:

   a) dry               b) attached          c) moist             d) none of the above

33. Infectious diseases that are easily transmitted by physical contact:

   a) contagious        b) communicable      c) antibodies        d) both a and b

34. Using a comb on a Guest with pityriasis is an example of:

   a) dilution          b) arrector pili     c) disinfection      d) contamination

35. In order to ensure your Guest has an even haircut, always perform _____ before you move onto the finish:

   a) blending          b) balancing         c) cross-checking    d) texturizing

36. In executing the 180° haircut, you most often begin in the interior or:

   a) crown             b) nape              c) fringe            d) side

37. A scaly, overlapping layer responsible for the porosity of the hair:

   a) cortex            b) cuticle           c) medulla           d) shaft

38. The purpose of _____ is to remove infected material from surfaces:

   a) decontamination   b) cleanliness       c) antibodies        d) antiseptic

39. Decontamination Method 1 involves cleaning tools with warm soapy water; next submerging them in a/an:

   a) EPA-registered    b) high-pressure     c) EPA-registered    d) ultra-violet
      disinfectant         steam unit           antiseptic           sanitizer

40. Decontamination Method 2 involves cleaning tools with warm, soapy water; next placing them in a/an:

   a) high-pressure     b) autoclave unit    c) ultra-violet      d) both a and b
      steam unit                                sanitizer

41. The projection or elevation you lift the hair at is known as:

   a) section           b) subsection        c) degree            d) partings

42. The removal of metal ions and/or impurities from water creates _____ water:

   a) mineral           b) deionized         c) salt              d) none of the above

# HAIRCUTTING
## STATE BOARD THEORY REVIEW

43. _____ is determined by the number of hairs per square inch:

a) Density     b) Length     c) Shape     d) Diameter

44. These cone-shaped elevations supply nourishment for the continued growth of the hair fiber:

a) lymph     b) dermal papillae     c) nerves     d) veins

45. _____ lines are not connected; they are independent lines that normally do not blend:

a) Disconnected     b) Blended     c) Staggered     d) Shattered

46. A bacterial invasion of the body that disrupts normal function of health:

a) virus     b) infection     c) disease     d) pain

47. An abnormality of body functions; services can be provided:

a) cowlick     b) disease     c) disorder     d) whorl

48. Edging is the technique of cutting around the _____ to create a clean line:

a) fringe     b) interior     c) hairline     d) none of the above

49. The epicranius is the broad muscle formed by the joining of the following:

a) occipitalis and frontalis     b) frontalis and temporalis     c) temporalis and occipitalis     d) occipitalis and corrugator

50. The epicranius is also known as:

a) frontalis     b) epicranium     c) occipito-frontalis     d) none of the above

51. The technical term for the scalp:

a) epicranium     b) frontalis     c) temporalis     d) occipitalis

52. The study of how equipment you use can best be designed for comfort, efficiency, safety, and productivity:

a) ergonomics     b) discipline     c) knowledge     d) none of the above

53. The art or process of creating etched designs within the hair:

a) cutting     b) sketching     c) etching     d) layering

# HAIRCUTTING
## STATE BOARD THEORY REVIEW

54. The experience of coming into contact with an environmental condition or social influence that has a harmful effect:

   a) exposure incident     b) intoxication     c) infection     d) none of the above

55. The gradual disappearance or blending of a line within the hair:

   a) fading     b) cutting     c) texturizing     d) tapering

56. Hair loss that is a part of nature and everyone experiences on an ongoing basis:

   a) broken hair     b) split ends     c) alopecia     d) fallen hair

57. The process of passing or putting something through a filter:

   a) filtration     b) pasteurizing     c) cleansing     d) none of the above

58. Fine textured hair has a small diameter / width and feels:

   a) rough     b) smooth     c) wavy     d) thin

59. Hair that is prone to breakage:

   a) fragilitas crinium     b) hypertrichosis     c) pityriasis     d) trichoptilosis

60. The bone that is located at the front of the head / skull and corresponds to the region known as the forehead:

   a) frontal     b) occipital     c) parietal     d) temporal

61. The frontalis muscle runs vertically on the _____, originating in tissues of the scalp above the hairline:

   a) forehead     b) chin     c) nape     d) nose

62. A hair stream creates:

   a) a natural part     b) fullness     c) a shift     d) short hair

63. Fungi, a single-celled or multicellular organism, include all of the following except:

   a) yeasts     b) molds     c) mildew     d) tinea

64. A boil on the skin:

   a) wart     b) vellus     c) furuncle     d) tick

65. The direction that the hair grows from the scalp:

    a) swirl        b) whorl        **c) growth pattern**        d) direction

66. The first section of hair that is cut to determine the length and/or shape:

    a) balance        b) form        **c) guideline**        d) shift

67. Hair bulb is the rounded, club-shaped part that is located at the end of the:

    **a) hair root**        b) hair follicle        c) nape        d) cocci

68. A small tubular pit in the epidermis, enclosing the base of a growing hair:

    **a) hair follicle**        b) hair shaft        c) hair bulb        d) hair structure

69. Water with a high content of dissolved minerals:

    a) soft water        **b) hard water**        c) rain water        d) none of the above

70. A disease of the scalp, characterized by a pink scalp with thick, whitish-yellowish crusts:

    a) canities        b) trichology        **c) tinea favosa**        d) none of the above

71. A line that is parallel to the floor and creates width in a design:

    a) an angle        b) diagonal        **c) horizontal**        d) vertical

72. A _____ is used to help retain moisture:

    **a) humectant**        b) glycerin        c) cleanser        d) none of the above

73. A substance that is dissolved, absorbed or mixed easily with water:

    a) humectant        b) hard water        c) soft water        **d) hydrophilic**

74. Immunity is a body's ability to resist _____ and _____; it may exist naturally or as a result of inoculation:

    a) virus and disorder        b) healthy white blood cells        **c) infection and disease**        d) none of the above

75. This occurs when disease-causing microorganisms invade a part of the body:

    **a) infection**        b) allergy        c) impurity        d) blight

76. In haircutting, the inside of the haircut is referred to as:

a) external     b) interior     c) top     d) bottom

77. The position of your Guest's head affects the _____ :

a) length     b) weight     c) texture     d) none of the above

78. Keratin is a fibrous, insoluble protein that is the main structural element in:

a) hair     b) nails     c) skin     d) all of the above

79. The depositing of keratin in skin cells (for example, in hair and nails) giving them a hard texture:

a) alopecia     b) keratinization     c) stacking     d) trichoptilosis

80. Lanugo hair, also known as _____, is the covering of soft downy hairs, especially those on a developing newborn infant:

a) vellus hair     b) fallen hair     c) terminal hair     d) longer hair

81. A muscle known as _____ is either of the two broad triangular muscles along the sides of the back:

a) platysma     b) pectoralis     c) latissimus dorsi     d) trapezius

82. The line(s) of haircutting, that create various design options are:

a) horizontal     b) vertical     c) diagonal     d) all of the above

83. Having an affinity for, tending to combine with, or capable of dissolving in lipids:

a) lipophilic     b) anionic     c) cationic     d) nonionic

84. A naturally occurring type of fungus:

a) hypertrichosis     b) trichoptilosis     c) malassezia     d) none of the above

85. Hair that has an average width and diameter is:

a) fine     b) medium     c) coarse     d) thin

86. A thin, superficial growth, produced on living plants or organic matter but does not cause human infections:

a) mildew     b) mold     c) fungus     d) moss

87. If your Guest has monilethrix, the hair shaft will appear:

a) shiny          b) smooth          c) strong          d) beaded, fragile, broken

88. The cocci bacteria rarely show active:

a) motility          b) measure          c) stationary          d) none of the above

89. The nape is the section of the head from the occipital bone to the:

a) forehead          b) chin          c) nose          d) hairline

90. The direction in which the hair moves or falls on the head:

a) shifted          b) disruptive          c) natural distribution          d) moveable

91. Microorganisms that are not disease producing:

a) non-pathogenic          b) pathogenic          c) diseases          d) disorders

92. Examples of nonporous surfaces that cannot be penetrated by water, air or fluids:

a) metal shears          b) workstations          c) sinks          d) all of the above

93. A cutting and/or texturizing technique that is used to reduce weight on the ends and blend layers:

a) slithering          b) feathering          c) chunking          d) notching

94. The saucer-shaped bone at the rear of the skull that sits directly above the nape:

a) frontal          b) occipital          c) parietal          d) temporal

95. The muscle that is located on the back of the head or skull:

a) occipitalis          b) parietal          c) temporal          d) none of the above

96. A muscle that covers parts of the skull. It consists of two parts: the occipital belly near the occipital bone, and the frontal belly near the frontal bone:

a) occipito-frontalis          b) occipitals          c) frontalis          d) none of the above

97. The outer edge or edges of a haircut:

a) shadow          b) texture          c) slither          d) outline

98. A cutting position that prevents hair from being lifted up off your hand and from being pushed out the front of the shears:

a) palm-to-palm     b) palm-down     c) cutting on top of fingers     d) none of the above

99. The point where the top of the head curves downward to become the sides of the head:

a) parietal ridge     b) front and back     c) left and right     d) none of the above

100. Lines traveling in the same direction and equal distance apart that never meet:

a) diagonal     b) horizontal     c) parallel     d) vertical

101. A _____ is known as living in or on another host organism, usually causing harm:

a) parasitic disease     b) parasitic infection     c) parasitic disorder     d) none of the above

102. An infestation with lice, specifically the head and body:

a) dandruff     b) itch mites     c) pediculosis capitis     d) ringworm

103. Bad bacteria that can cause disease:

a) probiotics     b) acidophilus     c) pathogenic     d) penicillin

104. The two bones, one on each side of the head, which form the entire crown and top sides:

a) frontal     b) occipital     c) parietal     d) temporal

105. Pityriasis commonly referring to flaking (or scaling) of the skin:

a) breakage     b) dandruff     c) knotted hair     d) split ends

106. A Guest having large, yellow, bran-like flakes on the scalp or skin has the following:

a) pityriasis steatoides     b) seborrheic dermatis     c) alopecia     d) both a and b

107. Platysma is the muscle that extends from the tip of the chin to the shoulder and lowers the:

a) eyes     b) ears     c) eyebrows     d) jaw and lip

108. Directing the hair out of its natural fall:

a) shifted distribution    b) stack    c) tension    d) weight

109. A texturizing technique using the tips of the shears to cut into the ends of a cutting line:

a) point cutting    b) chunking    c) slithering    d) razor rotation

110. Postpartum alopecia typically occurs after:

a) work    b) taking a big test    c) surgery    d) childbirth

111. The raising of a section of hair from the head:

a) projection    b) elevation    c) degree    d) all the above

112. Ringworm is a _____ disease of the skin or scalp, in which intensely itchy, ring-shaped patches develop:

a) fungal    b) parasite    c) cocci    d) bacilli

113. Scabies is a contagious skin disease marked by intense itching, inflammation, and red papules caused by:

a) dandruff    b) itch mites    c) lice    d) ringworm

114. These glands relate to or produce a waxy, yellowish body secretion (sebum) that lubricates the skin and scalp:

a) duct    b) endocrine    c) sebaceous    d) sudoriferous

115. Sectioning divides areas of hair in order to be able to:

a) part and apply    b) manage and control    c) section and divide    d) copy and apply

116. The _____ - _____ - _____ is a technique used to blend weight lines:

a) scissors-over-comb    b) razor-over-comb    c) clipper-over-comb    d) all of the above

117. The bony part of the head that encases the brain and includes the bones of the face and jaw:

a) neck    b) forehead    c) skull    d) face

118. Used to remove bulk, this texturizing technique adds mobility within the haircut by sliding down or along the surface of the hair:

    a) slithering / slicing    b) texturizing    c) tapering    d) beveling

119. The purpose of the _____ cutting technique is to remove bulk, add movement and frame areas around the face:

    a) texturizing    b) beveling    c) slide    d) tapering

120. _____ water is naturally occurring or treated water in which soap lathers easily because of the low levels of mineral content:

    a) Soft    b) Hard    c) Soft and hard    d) None of the above

121. The _____ bone is one of the seven bones that join to form the cranium:

    a) frontal    b) sphenoid    c) neck    d) jaw

122. Spirilla is a _____ shaped or curved bacteria:

    a) flat    b) square    c) spiral    d) rectangle

123. Staphylococci bacterial cells form _____, causing abscesses, pustules and boils:

    a) clusters    b) groups    c) pairs    d) chains

124. A guideline that does not move around the head:

    a) moving    b) shifting    c) stationary    d) traveling

125. Sternocleidomastoideus is the muscle of the neck that lowers and rotates the:

    a) shoulder    b) head    c) jaw    d) arms

126. Streptococci are bacterial cells that form in _____, causing blood poisoning and strep throat:

    a) long chains    b) clusters    c) ropes    d) none of the above

127. A wetting agent that has the ability to dissolve in water and removes dirt from surfaces like hair:

    a) lathering agent    b) surfactant    c) detergent    d) styling aid

128. A cutting technique that blends hair from a shorter length to a longer length as you move up the head:

   a) slithering          b) tapering          c) beveling          d) chunking

129. The resting phase of hair growth is the _____ stage:

   a) anagen          b) catagen          c) keratin          d) telogen

130. Telogen effluvium is hair loss that is:

   a) due to normal hair     b) due to aging          c) expected          d) premature or sudden

131. The bones that form the side of the head in the ear region:

   a) frontal          b) occipital          c) parietal          d) temporal

132. A broad, radiating muscle, situated at the side of the head:

   a) temporalis          b) parietal          c) occipital          d) frontal

133. Applying pressure to the hair is known as:

   a) elevation          b) shift          c) tension          d) weight

134. Long, coarse, pigmented hair:

   a) fine          b) lanugo          c) terminal          d) vellus

135. The diameter of each hair strand, described as fine, medium, or coarse:

   a) density          b) elasticity          c) porosity          d) texture

136. _____ helps to blend lines or remove excess bulk without changing the shape of the haircut:

   a) Channeling          b) Texturizing          c) Slicing          d) Beveling

137. The technical term for ringworm:

   a) pediculosis          b) pityriasis          c) scabies          d) tinea

138. Tinea capitis is a fungal infection of the skin and scalp characterized by _____ or spots at the opening of the hair follicle:

   a) red papules          b) yellow patches          c) bruised spots          d) all the above

139. A Guest with tinea favosa has:

a) a fungal infection    b) a pink scalp    c) thick, whitish-yellow crusts on the scalp    d) all the above

140. Hair loss through repetitive and excessive pulling or stretching of the hair:

a) alopecia totalis    b) alopecia universalis    c) androgenic alopecia    d) traction alopecia

141. The muscle that runs from the upper back to the back of the neck:

a) pectoralis    b) trapezius    c) platysma    d) tendon

142. A guideline that moves around the head:

a) cross-checking    b) permanent    c) stationary    d) traveling

143. Trichology is the study of _____ and its diseases and disorders:

a) nails    b) feet    c) hair    d) skin

144. The scientific term for 'split ends':

a) fragilitas crinium    b) hypertrichosis    c) pityriasis    d) trichoptilosis

145. Trichorrehexis nodosa is characterized by:

a) brittleness    b) nodular swellings    c) easy breakage    d) all the above

146. A set of guidelines published by OSHA that require an employer and employee to assume that all human blood and body fluids are infectious:

a) universal precautions    b) safety data sheets    c) personal protective equipment    d) exposure incidents

147. Pigmented hair located on the scalp, arms, legs, nose and ears:

a) terminal    b) vellus    c) keratin    d) none of the above

148. A line that extends straight up from the floor:

a) diagonal    b) horizontal    c) parallel    d) vertical

# HAIRCUTTING
## STATE BOARD THEORY REVIEW

149. A virus is a submicroscopic, parasitic particle that causes:

a) disorders      b) diseases      c) monilethrix      d) trichoptilosis

150. In _____ cutting, the spacing of the shear's teeth, the depth of the teeth, and the angle of the blades combine to create special effects on the hair strands:

a) weave      b) carving      c) beveling      d) slithering

151. A concentration of hair within an area that gives the appearance of heaviness and density:

a) elevation      b) shift      c) tension      d) weight line

152. Whorl is a growth pattern where hair moves in a _____ pattern:

a) circular      b) square      c) straight      d) none of the above

**My Need To Know Notes:**

_____

_____

_____

_____

_____

_____

_____

_____

_____

_____

_____

_____

_____

_____

# MY NEED TO KNOW notes:

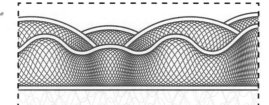

PARTME

u OF PROFESSIONAL

PO Box 39(

*Cosmetolo*

SAMPL

123 AN

CITY, ST/

# HAIRCOLORING

# HAIRCOLORING SAFETY AND DISINFECTION

Safety must come first when servicing your Guests. There are many precautions to consider when performing a haircolor service. Below are a few of the steps necessary for all haircolor services.

**Fill in the blanks, and describe how to perform each.**

## Predisposition /Patch Test

determines if an individual is allergic to haircolor products containing an aniline derivative.

## Patch test

is the industry accepted term for predisposition test.

**Steps to perform a proper patch test:**

1. Set up station
2. Select the area to be tested /cleanse + dry
3. Mix small amount of hair color
4. Put on gloves
5. apply small amount of color with cotton-tipped
6. Do not disturb/remove for 24-48 hours
7. Examine test area
8. Document the date of patch test + results

## Preliminary Strand Test

is the second step in a haircolor consultation, done as a safety precaution to avoid excessive damage and ensure Guest satisfaction prior to performing the entire service.

**Steps to perform a preliminary strand test:**

1. Set up station
2. Drape guest
3. put on gloves
4. take a ½ inch
5. Place hair on foil/apply the color
6. Process haircolor
7. Wipe color
8. Document formula

# HAIRCOLORING SAFETY AND DISINFECTION

Processing Strand Test
will determine if the haircolor is absorbing or lifting evenly during the service.

**Steps to perform a processing strand test:**
1. take small subsection
2. wipe free of haircolor/lightener
3. view in natural light

Proper Draping is important to follow based upon the desired service.

**Below are the 4 steps to ensure your Guest is adequately protected. Number the photos in the correct order as you would perform them.**

2

3

4

1

# HAIR STRUCTURE

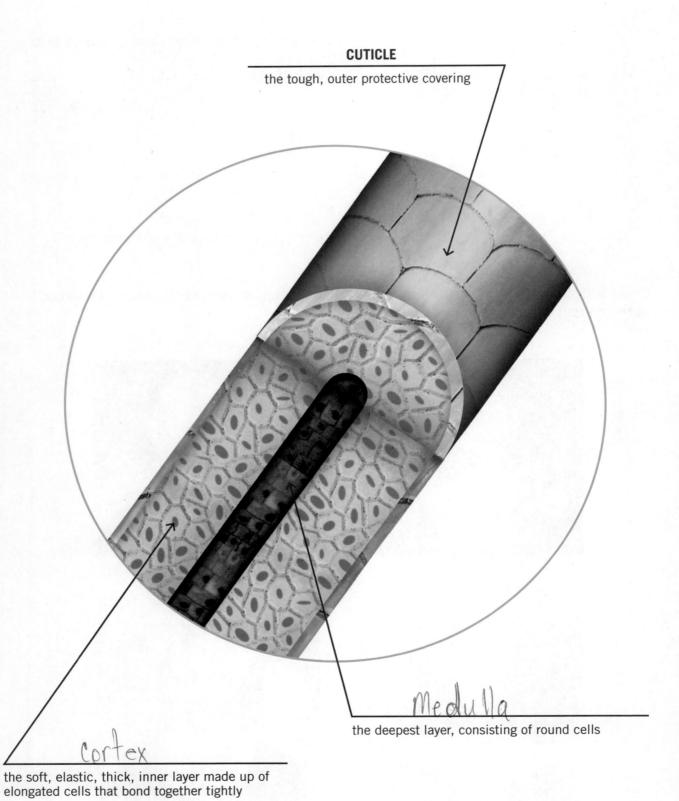

**CUTICLE**
the tough, outer protective covering

Medulla
the deepest layer, consisting of round cells

Cortex
the soft, elastic, thick, inner layer made up of elongated cells that bond together tightly

# HAIR PIGMENT

__Melanin__
the coloring matter that provides natural color to the hair, skin and eyes

__Eumelanin__
produces brown to black pigments in the hair

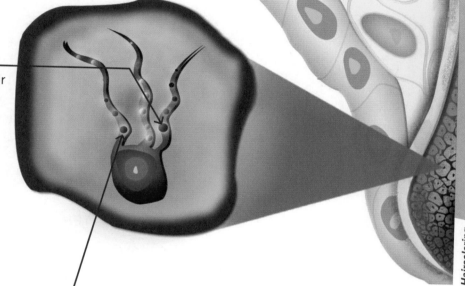

__Pheomelanin__
produces red to yellow pigments in the hair

The combination of eumelanin and pheomelanin inside one cell is known as __Mixed Melanin__.

__Canities__ occurs by a gradual slowing down of melanin production in the cortex; commonly known as gray hair.

# CHEMISTRY PRINCIPLES

**CHEMISTRY IS:**

the science that deals with the composition, structures, and properties of matter and how matter changes under different chemical conditions

Light, electricity and sound are not a __chemical__, which is a substance used in, or produced by, the process of chemistry.

__Organic__ __chemistry__ studies matter that contains carbon and is living or at one time was alive.

**Examples:** _pesticides, fertilizers_

__Inorganic__ __chemistry__ studies substances that do not contain carbon and were never living or alive.

**Examples:** _pure water, minerals, metals, clean air._

**MATTER IS:**

substance that has mass and occupies space.

__Element__ is <u>the simplest form of matter</u> and <u>cannot be broken down into a simpler substance.</u>

__Atom__ is the smallest chemical part of an element, which all matter consists of.

**Explain in your own words the role that chemistry plays in haircoloring:**

_____

_____

_____

# THE MAKING OF AN ATOM

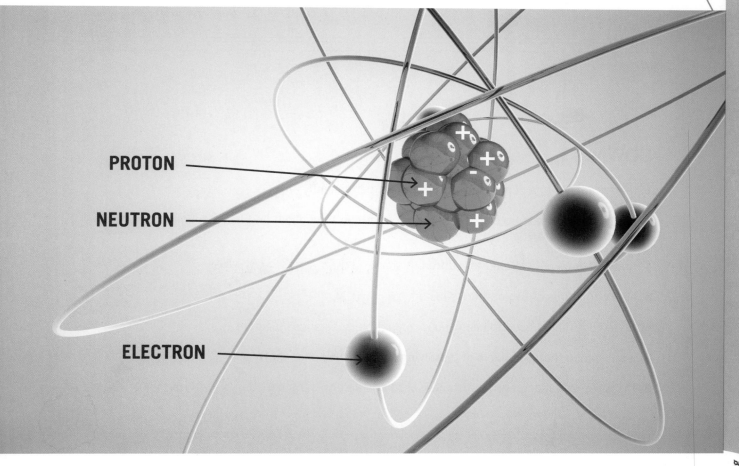

Protons _____ positively charged particles found in the nucleus

Neutrons _____ neutral particles found in the nucleus

Electrons _____ negatively charged particles that revolve around the nucleus

Ions _____ atoms containing an excess amount of electrons or not enough electrons in their orbiting paths

Molecule _____ created when one or more atoms combine and retain their chemical and physical properties to form matter

Compound Molecule _____ also known as compounds, are a chemical substance consisting of atoms or ions of two or more elements

# CHEMISTRY SUBSTANCES | CROSSWORD PUZZLE

## DOWN

**1.** matter altered to a completely different form permanently *chemical change*

**3.** matter that is made up of the same type of particle throughout and has a definite chemical and physical property

**4.** matter temporarily altered to a different shape *physical change*

**5.** stable mixtures of two or more substances *Solutions*

**6.** ingredient that is used to keep two incompatible substances together

**8.** a substance that is capable of dissolving another substance *Solvent*

**9.** the rapid oxidation of any substance, accompanied by the production of heat and light *Combustion*

## ACROSS

**2.** occurs without a chemical reaction or change to the matter *physical properties*

**4.** combinations of two or more substances that physically combine *physical mixtures*

**7.** the chemical reaction that occurs when oxygen is released from a substance *oxidation*

**10.** suspension of one liquid in a second liquid with which the first will not mix *Emulsion*

**11.** causes a chemical reaction and change to the matter *chemical properties*

**12.** mixture in which small particles of a substance are dispersed throughout a gas or liquid *Suspension*

Haircoloring

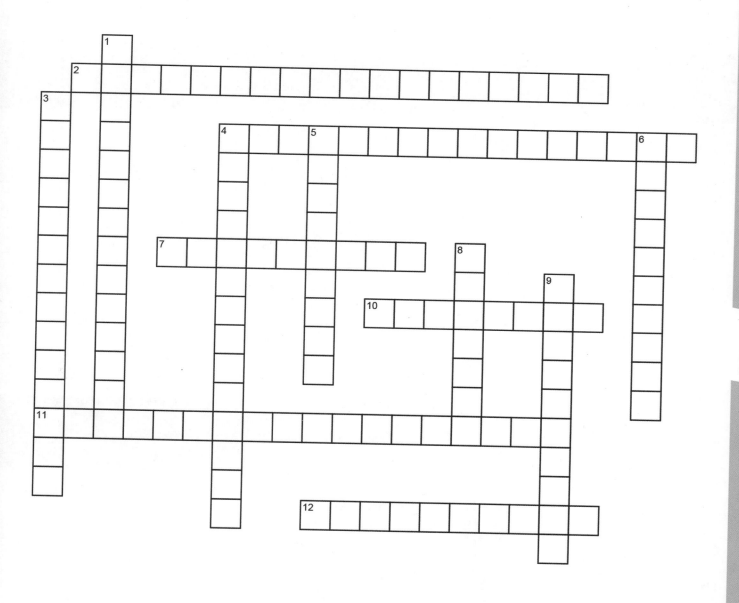

# COMMON SALON PRODUCTS AND pH

## The 3 A's used in Haircoloring

*Ammonia* _____ is an organic compound of colorless gas with a strong, pungent odor.

*Alkanolamines* _____ are used to neutralize acids or raise the pH.

*Aniline Derivatives* _____ are small compounds found in permanent haircolor.

## pH SCALE

Referring back to the pH scale in your textbook, determine the pH of each product listed below. Then, list the products you could use to help balance and/or restore the pH.

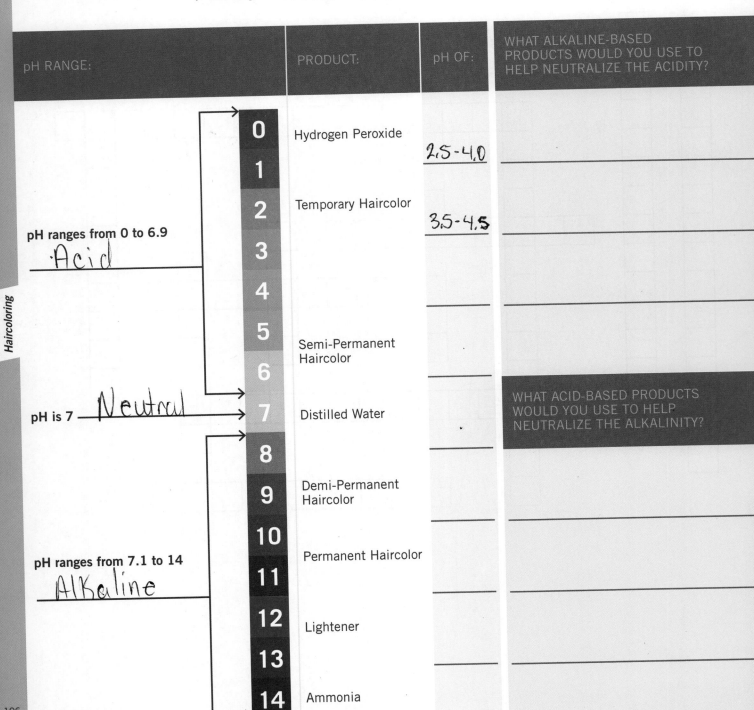

| pH RANGE: | PRODUCT: | pH OF: | WHAT ALKALINE-BASED PRODUCTS WOULD YOU USE TO HELP NEUTRALIZE THE ACIDITY? |
|---|---|---|---|
| | **0** Hydrogen Peroxide | 2.5-4.0 | |
| | **1** | | |
| | **2** Temporary Haircolor | 3.5-4.5 | |
| pH ranges from 0 to 6.9 *Acid* | **3** | | |
| | **4** | | |
| | **5** Semi-Permanent Haircolor | | |
| | **6** | | |
| pH is 7 *Neutral* | **7** Distilled Water | | WHAT ACID-BASED PRODUCTS WOULD YOU USE TO HELP NEUTRALIZE THE ALKALINITY? |
| | **8** | | |
| | **9** Demi-Permanent Haircolor | | |
| pH ranges from 7.1 to 14 *Alkaline* | **10** Permanent Haircolor | | |
| | **11** | | |
| | **12** Lightener | | |
| | **13** | | |
| | **14** Ammonia | | |

# UNDERSTANDING COLORS | Experiment with the primary colors to create secondary and tertiary colors.

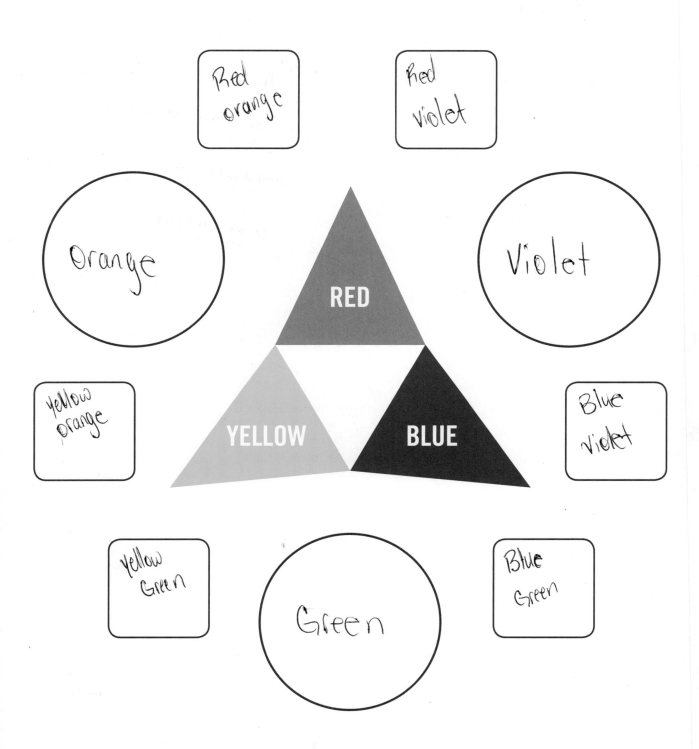

Red orange

Red violet

Orange

Violet

Yellow orange

Blue violet

YELLOW

RED

BLUE

Yellow Green

Blue Green

Green

# BASIC COLOR FUNDAMENTALS

The __Law of Color__ is a system that provides the understanding of color relationships.

A __Color Wheel__ is a support tool for the Law of Color.

---

**Primary**

the 3 basic starting colors by which all other colors are created
**Red, Blue & Yellow**

**Secondary**

colors that can be made by mixing two primary colors
**Violet, Green & Orange**

**Tertiary**

colors that are made by mixing primary colors with an analogous secondary color
**Red-Orange, Blue-Green, Blue-Violet, etc.**

**Complementary**

colors that are directly across from each other on the color wheel
**Blue & Orange, Red & Green, Violet & Yellow**

---

**Use colored pencils or crayons to complete the color wheel.**

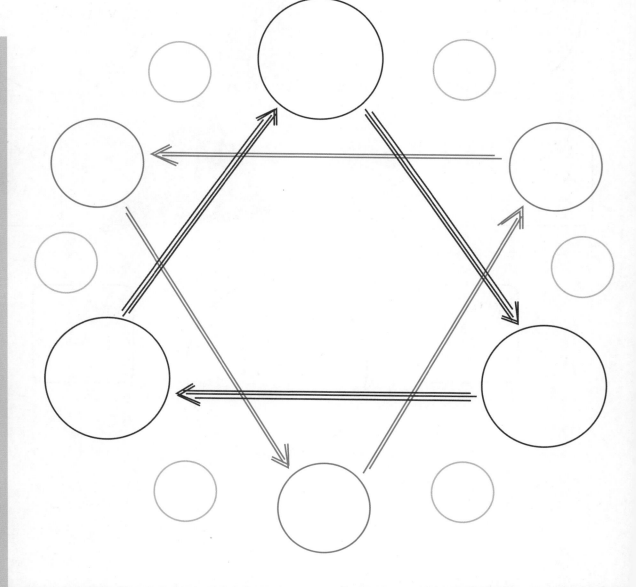

## NEUTRAL COLORS

**BLACK**

**WHITE**

**GRAY**

**BROWN**

Haircoloring

# COLOR VALUES

| | TINTS | SHADES | VALUE |
|---|---|---|---|
| _Tone_ also known as _Hue_, is the balance of color | Created by adding white to a color | Created by adding gray or black to a color | The darkness or lightness of a color |

## MONOCHROMATIC COLOR SCHEME

Using colored pencils or crayons, create a monochromatic color scheme within the chart.

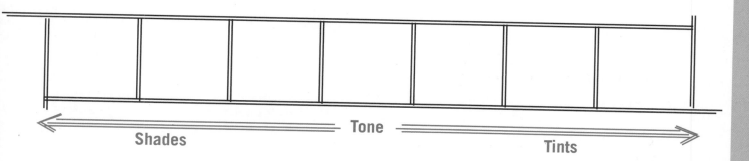

⟵ Shades ═══ Tone ═══ Tints ⟶

Beginning with the 3 primary colors, white and black, create a picture of a color scheme.

# HAIRCOLOR CATEGORIES

## HAIRCOLOR CATEGORIES

### Non - Oxidative
creates a physical change to the hair; deposit only haircolor; lasts 4 to 6 washes.

### Oxidative
creates a chemical change to the hair; requires a developer; longer-lasting results.

**Types of non-oxidative haircolor:**

Temporary (Semi)

coats the hair surface, covering only the cuticle

Semi-Permanent

penetrates the cuticle layer; will gradually fade

**Types of oxidative haircolor:**

_____

penetrates the cuticle and partially into the cortex; mixed with a low volume developer

_____

penetrates the cuticle and cortex; can deposit and lift natural pigments

| ADVANTAGES | DISADVANTAGES |
|---|---|
| no permanent change | Color can stain skin |
| Tones down grey hair | Cannot lighten hair |
| No mix required | |
| reduce yellow undertones | |
| retouching not required | |
| last 4-6 weeks | |

| ADVANTAGES | DISADVANTAGES |
|---|---|
| | |
| | |
| | |
| | |
| | |

Haircoloring

# ADDITIONAL HAIRCOLOR AND LIGHTENER CHOICES

**NON-PROFESSIONAL**

1. _____

2. _____

What is a metallic salt test?

_____

_____

_____

How do you perform a metallic salt test?

_____

_____

_____

**PROFESSIONAL**

1. _____

2. _____

3. Concentrate

    a. _____

    b. _____

4. _____

5. _____

6. _____

    a. _____

    b. _____

**Complete the diagram below:**
*Middle – list the similarities; Outside rings – list the differences.*

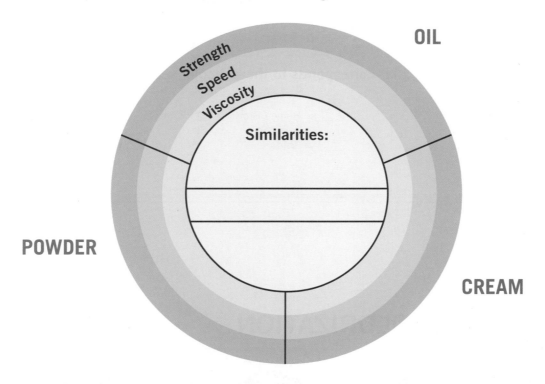

Explain in your own words what *Redox* is and how it affects haircolor.

_____

_____

# FOUNDATION TO FORMULATION

__Developer__ is an oxidizing agent, also known as hydrogen peroxide or catalyst.

| | |
|---|---|
| Same level OR 1 level higher than the base level (Minimal lift) | **10 volume** |
| 1 to 2 levels lighter than the base level (Standard volume; Gray coverage) | **20 volume** |
| 2 to 3 levels lighter than the base level | **30 volume** |
| 3 to 4 levels lighter than the base level (Maximum lift) | **40 volume** |

__Level system__ is used to determine the lightness or darkness of any color.

__Level__ is used to 'measure' the degree of lightness to darkness of a color.

*Typically, a Level System has two components:*

__Number__ indicates the degree of lightness to darkness.

__Letter__ indicates the tone and/or shade direction.

## TONES / SHADES

**Fill in the correct letter that corresponds to the haircolor series.**

| | | | | | |
|---|---|---|---|---|---|
| _N_ = Natural | | _B_ = Beige / Brown | | _A_ = Ash | |
| _R_ = Red | | _G_ = Gold | | _V_ = Violet | |

# STAGES OF DECOLORIZATION

1 BLACK  2 DARK RED BROWN  3 RED BROWN  4 RED  5 RED ORANGE

# FOUNDATION TO FORMULATION

*undertone*

~~Base Color~~ _____ is the warm or cool tones present within the predominant haircolor.

**Fill in the blanks with the correct undertone. Then indicate what tone would control or neutralize the undesired undertone.**

| Natural Level | Undertone | Controlling Color |
|---|---|---|
| 1 Black | Red Brown | Ash, Ash, Ash |
| 2 Natural Black / Darkest Brown | _Red_ Brown | Ash |
| 3 Dark Brown | Red | Ash |
| 4 Medium Brown | _Red_ Orange | Ash |
| 5 Light Brown | Dark Orange | Ash |
| 6 Lightest Brown / Darkest Blonde | Medium _Orange_ / Orange | Ash, Violet |
| 7 Dark Blonde | Light Orange / Orange Gold | Violet |
| 8 Medium Blonde | Gold / Yellow Orange | Violet |
| 9 Light Blonde | _Yellow_ | Violet |
| 10 Lightest Blonde | Pale Yellow | Violet, Violet, Violet |
| 11 Extra Light Blonde | Palest Yellow | Violet, Violet |

## FORMULATION GUIDELINES

**Using a mannequin or classmate, identify the following:**

1. _____ = Natural Level

2. _____ = Target Level / Tone

3. _____ = Undertone

4. _____ = % of Gray

5. _____ = Developer Strength

## MEASURING / MIXING / TIMING

*Always read and follow*

_____

*directions!*

When the cuticle scales are lying flat, making the amount of liquid absorbed by the hair minimal, the hair is said to be _____.

| 6 DARK ORANGE | 7 LIGHT ORANGE | 8 GOLD | 9 YELLOW | 10 PALE YELLOW |

1. __Decolorization__ occurs when haircolor is diffused from the hair

2. _____ placement of haircolor on selected pieces or sections of hair to create dimension

3. __Double Process Haircolor__ a two-step technique requiring the hair to be lightened then toned

4. __Foiling__ technique of weaving or slicing out selected portions of hair, then placing that hair on a piece of foil

5. __Glaze__ used to add shine and/or tone to the hair

6. __Highlighting__ lifting selected pieces of artificial or natural hair color

7. __Line of demarcation__ visible line or band between haircolor or lightener applications

8. __Lowlighting__ depositing haircolor to selected pieces of hair

9. __Pre-Softening__ recommended for gray hair and/or resistant hair to allow better haircolor penetration

10. __Single process retouch__ application of haircolor to new growth only

11. __Single-process__ application of haircolor to lighten or deposit in one-step

12. __slicing__ technique is performed by taking out a thin, straight portion of hair within a section

13. __Special Effects__ creates texture and dimension using haircolor

14. __Virgin Haircolor__ first time haircolor application

15. __Weaving__ technique is performed by taking zigzag portions of hair within a section of hair

# HAIRCOLOR APPLICATIONS, PROCEDURES AND TECHNIQUES | WORD SEARCH

```
N L I N E O F D E M A R C A T I O N
O B D Y M M C L N P P N P T M M T K
I X L D H L O W L I G H T I N G H S
T R D O U B L E P R O C E S S G G S
A Q S R C Q M V H X L D T R K L R E
Z N P C F N G Y M C Y B X G A F T C
I K E G G P K P Y U Z K N N G L O R
R Z C K L G M R N R O O M N K Y R O
O K I G A K N T E Y R I T I P B C P
L X A B Z V H I F S S N C E M P C E
O R L L I L G F V N O I G G R F C L
C G E Q N R P F E A L N X R J T G
E K F T G N M O S E T K V R X N
D C F R R B I Z I V W M E D L Z I
K H E M K D M C B H L N K N N J H S
T K C L D G N I T H G I L H G I H J
L J T T B W G K H Q M T N T L T N P
N D S H N I G R I V D R G G G M B G
```

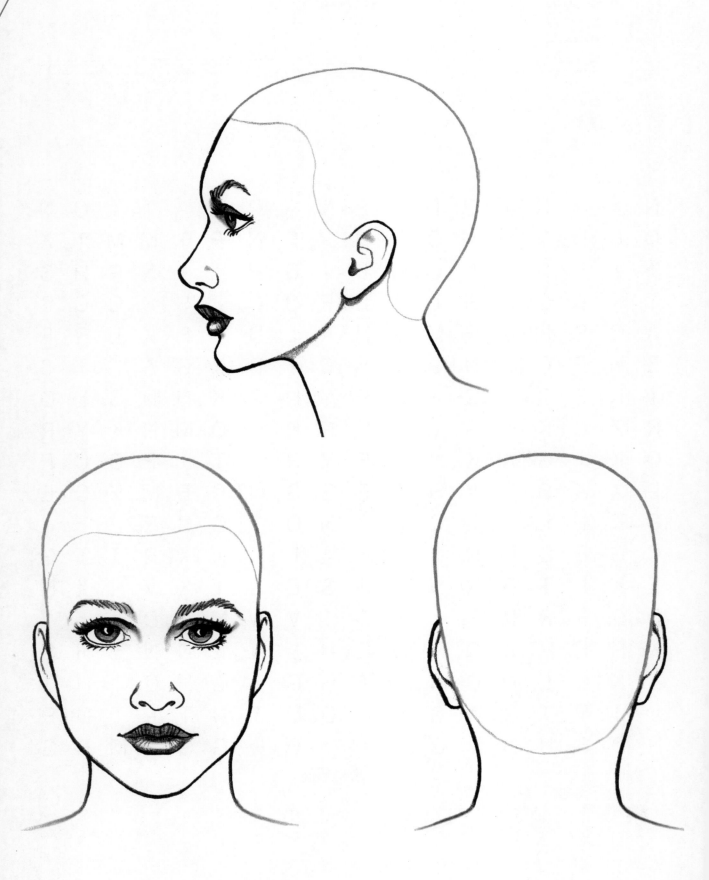

# WORKSHOP
# standards

## Safety and Infection Control:

Disinfect work station *(before and after each service)*
Set up work station with required, clean service tools

## Consultation:

Scalp Analysis: ☐oily ☐normal ☐dry ☐abrasions
Hair Analysis: ☐density ☐texture ☐elasticity ☐porosity
Drape: neck strip, towel, cape, towel

## Shampoo Bowl Safety:

Maintain control of nozzle at all times, with constant temperature check
Appropriate amount of product is dispensed
Rinse product(s) thoroughly from scalp and hair
Disinfect shampoo bowl and water nozzle

## Color Application:

Neatly section and clip hair into 4 quadrants
Neatly apply protective cream around hairline
Remove any haircolor on skin
Process according to manufacturer's directions

### Virgin Application:

Apply color using ¼" partings
Proper use of applicator brush *(use both sides to ensure coverage and extension of product)*
Partings with applied haircolor – carefully and neatly placed away from face

### Retouch Application:

Apply haircolor to new growth only
No excessive overlapping onto previously colored hair

### Lightener Application:

Apply lightener to ⅛" partings, staying ½" away from scalp and porous ends
No overlapping onto previously colored / lightened hair *(if applicable)*

### Foiling:

Take ⅛" to ¼" partings
Proper placement, positioning and use of foil
No bleeding of haircolor or lightener onto scalp

## Finishing of Service:

Apply appropriate amount and type of fixative(s) to damp / wet hair
Dry hair 80% before using styling brushes
Maintain proper control and temperature of all electrical tools
Complete style as desired
Recommend at-home maintenance product(s)

Haircoloring

# DEVELOPING YOUR HAIRCOLORING COMMUNICATION AND SOLUTION SKILLS

What consultation question(s) will you have prepared to ask your Guest for the following:

Single Process:_____

Highlights:_____

Retouch:_____

_____

## How would you respond to the following scenarios: What would you say, do, and/or ask?

Your Guest informs you that they want to enhance their existing haircolor by adding warmth.

_____

_____

Your Guest cannot continue their regular 6 week haircolor maintenance appointments.

_____

_____

Your Guest tells you that after their last haircolor service, they experienced some breakage / hair loss.

_____

_____

Your Guest's haircolor has faded several levels since their last visit 6 weeks ago.

_____

_____

Haircoloring

## SERVICE RECOMMENDATIONS

What styling recommendations will you discuss with your Guest for the following and why?

Single Process:_____

Highlights:_____

Retouch:_____

## MAINTENANCE RECOMMENDATIONS

When discussing a maintenance routine with your Guest, how often will you suggest they rebook for the following services?

Single Process:_____

Highlights:_____

Retouch:_____

## PRODUCT RECOMMENDATIONS

What product recommendations will you discuss with your Guest and why?

_____

_____

_____

Shampoo:_____

Conditioner:_____

Styling:_____

Finishing:_____

# SITUATIONAL SCENARIOS

**1.** Your Guest has arrived for a pre-booked haircolor appointment. You greet your Guest and walk them back to your station. Once seated, your Guest begins to ask you questions about their last haircoloring appointment, such as, "Did you change my haircolor formula? Did the salon change haircolor brands?" Why would your Guest be asking these types of questions?

    **a)** Your Guest is just the inquisitive type
    **b)** Your Guest is prying for private information
    **c)** Your Guest may or may not have been happy with their last haircolor service
    **d)** Your Guest wants to give the haircolor formulation to a friend

**2.** Your 5:00 pm appointment is a new Guest scheduled for a single process haircolor. You have booked 1½ hours for this appointment. Your Guest arrives, and when greeting your Guest, you notice that their haircolor service will be a corrective haircolor, not a single process haircolor. What do you do?

    **a)** Immediately tell your Guest that you do not have enough time to service them
    **b)** Explain that you did not book the appointment and that you do not do corrective haircolor
    **c)** Walk them back to your chair, begin the consultation and hope for the best
    **d)** Walk them back to your chair, begin the consultation and recommend the appropriate steps necessary, including the time required for you to adequately service your Guest's request

**3.** During the haircolor consultation with your Guest, you notice that their scalp is dry and has abrasions. How should you proceed?

    **a)** Make a scene, saying "Oh my, there is no way we can do this haircolor"
    **b)** Quietly discuss your findings with your Guest; recommend a specific shampoo, conditioner and/or treatment that can be done at home; and reschedule the haircolor appointment
    **c)** Ask your Guest if they frequently shampoo their hair
    **d)** Tell your Guest you cannot service them, but will refer them to another stylist

**4.** When consulting with your Guest, Mary, she states that she does not want to see any warmth or gray in her hair. What steps will you need to take when formulating Mary's haircolor?

    **a)** Explain to Mary that you can only achieve one of the two requests
    **b)** Determine the natural level, desired tone / shade, undertone, percentage of gray, and developer strength to achieve the correct haircolor formulation
    **c)** Use a haircolor that is 2 to 3 levels darker than Mary's natural hair color
    **d)** Determine Mary's natural level and use a gray coverage haircolor in the same level

**5.** When consulting with your Guest, they tell you that their hair turns a greenish color every time they receive a highlighting service? What would your recommendation be?

    **a)** Not to have a highlighting service
    **b)** Recommend using an A (ash) series
    **c)** Recommend using a warm tone
    **d)** Recommend your Guest return to their previous salon and make a complaint

**6.** Gina, your regular Guest, calls you after her haircolor appointment and says her red haircolor has faded drastically, even though she went to a local store and bought the haircolor maintenance shampoo you suggested. How should you respond?

    **a)** Invite Gina to return and you will redo her haircolor at no charge

    **b)** Explain to Gina that you cannot guarantee the longevity of her haircolor unless she has purchased the recommended products from your salon, as you discussed with her during her appointment

    **c)** Tell Gina that for her next haircolor appointment you will add more red color to her formula

    **d)** Complain to Gina that you do not like using the haircolor brand that your salon uses because it's known to fade

**7.** After a haircolor service on your new Guest, you realize that the haircolor did not take evenly. What would have been a preventative step to avoid this mishap?

    **a)** Complete a thorough consultation, including a scalp and hair analysis, with a preliminary strand test

    **b)** Shampoo and condition the hair prior to service, invigorating the scalp

    **c)** Heavily saturate the hair with haircolor product

    **d)** Use a haircolor formula 2 levels or more darker

**8.** Your regular Guest, Ann, arrives for her appointment. You greet and walk Ann back to your chair. Ann begins the conversation by saying that she recently colored her hair at home and was unhappy with the yellow-orange results. Ann wants her hair returned to her natural hair color. What do you do?

    **a)** Apologize and offer to fix it for free

    **b)** Begin with the consultation, assessing Ann's hair and what steps will be needed to correct the haircolor, explaining that it will be a corrective color application

    **c)** Recommend a box color that Ann can purchase and redo at home

    **d)** Give Ann a lecture about haircolor so she can do it herself

**9.** When performing your Guest's scalp and hair analysis, you notice a line of demarcation on their hair. As you follow through with the consultation and ask your Guest about previous haircolor services, your Guest states that they have never had any professional haircolor services before. How do you proceed?

    **a)** Continue with your Guest's requested haircolor service

    **b)** State to your Guest that they have a line of demarcation and ask how they achieved it

    **c)** Ask your Guest if they have used store bought haircolor and perform a preliminary strand test

    **d)** Refuse to do the service

**10.** Sarah, your newly acquired Guest, wants to change her vibrant red haircolor to blonde. As you proceed with the consultation, Sarah states she is not concerned with the integrity of her hair and insists on getting her hair blonde. How do you proceed?

    **a)** Explain to Sarah that it will take several steps and a few hours, but you will get her to the desired blonde

    **b)** Explain to Sarah that it will take several steps and visits to achieve the desired results

    **c)** Tell Sarah that her request is not obtainable

    **d)** Discuss the possibilities with Sarah, as well as, the time and total cost of service(s). Next, perform a strand test, sharing the results with Sarah, and provide your professional opinion

# practical PREP

*Each skill will be checked by your Educator and feedback will be provided.*
*Color and Lightener are mock applications. Met Skill = 1 point / Not Met Skill = 0 points*

POINTS

## Safety and Disinfection:

Disinfects work station *(before and after each service)*
Station set up with required tools
Drapes for a chemical service
Performs scalp and hair analysis
Neatly divides and clips hair into 4 quadrants
Applies protective gloves
Applies protective cream around hairline and ears *(optional)*
**Feedback:**

## Virgin Haircolor Application *(right back section)*:

Uses ¼" partings
Application and control of haircolor *(neatly applied around hairline, no dripping)*
Applies haircolor ½" from scalp and ½" from porous ends
Completes application of haircolor to scalp area and ends
Proper handling of tool(s) *(bowl / brush)*
**Feedback:**

## Retouch Haircolor Application *(left back section)*:

Uses ¼" partings
Application and control of haircolor to new growth only *(neatly applied around hairline, no dripping)*
Proper handling of tool(s) *(applicator bottle)*
**Feedback:**

## Lightener Application *(left front section)*:

Uses ⅛" partings
Placement of lightener on hair, staying ½" from scalp and ends *(cold shaft)*
Control of lightener *(neatly applied, no dripping)*
Proper handling of tool(s)*(bowl / brush)*
**Feedback:**

## Foiling:

Slicing Technique *(bottom half of right front section)*:
　　¼" straight partings
　　Positioning and control of foil
　　Placement of color – no bleeding / swelling of color / lightener onto scalp
Weaving Technique *(top half of right front section)*:
　　¼" zigzag partings
　　Positioning and control of foil
　　Placement of color – no bleeding / swelling of color / lightener onto scalp
**Feedback:**

Haircoloring

# HAIRCOLORING
## STATE BOARD THEORY REVIEW

1. Alkalinity pH range is:

   a) 7.0 to 14      b) 7.1 to 14      c) 8.0 to 14      d) 8.1 to 14

2. Bleach is also known as:

   a) lightener      b) decolorizer      c) neither a nor b      d) both a and b

3. One part of a group of viscous (thick), water-soluble amino alcohols:

   a) aniline derivatives      b) alkanolamines      c) ammonia      d) acetone

4. The transformation of composition, structures and properties of matter:

   a) electricity      b) chemistry      c) anatomy      d) physiology

5. _____ haircolors are divided into two types of dye molecules:

   a) Metallic dye      b) Compound dye      c) Aniline derivative      d) Alkanolamine

6. Applying an oxidative haircolor over a metallic dye is an example of:

   a) oxidation      b) explosion      c) combustion      d) corrosion

7. _____ occurs by the slowing down of melanin production in the cortex of the hair:

   a) Lightening      b) Toning      c) Alopecia      d) Canities

8. Products that are acidic have a pH range of:

   a) 0 to 5.9      b) 0 to 6.0      c) 1.0 to 6.0      d) all of the above

9. Catalyst is also known as:

   a) hydrogen peroxide      b) oxidative haircolor      c) volume      d) none of the above

10. A _____ substance is a form of matter that has constant composition and specific properties:

   a) property      b) pure      c) haircolor      d) chemical

11. The colorless gas with a strong odor that divides oxidative colors into two categories:

   a) ammonia      b) alkaline      c) acid      d) alcohol

12. The color wheel is a tool that:

   a) supports the law of color      b) shows how colors are created      c) helps to identify complementary color      d) all of the above

# HAIRCOLORING
## STATE BOARD THEORY REVIEW

13. A long lasting semi-permanent haircolor is known as:

   a) temporary      b) semi-permanent      c) demi-permanent      d) permanent

14. _____ are used to neutralize undesirable colors:

   a) Tertiary colors      b) Complementary colors      c) Monochromatic colors      d) Analogous colors

15. While lifting natural hair color, the hair will go through stages of:

   a) decolorization      b) haircoloring      c) color balancing      d) dimensional coloring

16. These are also known as lighteners:

   a) haircolor molecules      b) metallic dyes      c) decolorizers      d) vegetable dyes

17. Concentrates are classified into two types:

   a) intensifiers and pure colors      b) drabbers and intensifiers      c) drabbers and pure colors      d) intensifiers and complementary colors

18. Compound is also known as:

   a) electrons      b) pure substances      c) compound molecule      d) solutions

19. Hydrogen peroxide that contains both two hydrogen and two oxygen molecules is an example of:

   a) compound      b) complementary      c) monochromatic      d) corrosion

20. The outermost layer of hair that is protective:

   a) cuticle      b) cortex      c) medulla      d) hair shaft

21. Contributing pigment is also known as:

   a) true color      b) undertone      c) dominant pigment      d) warm color

22. The layer of hair that contains melanin:

   a) cuticle      b) cortex      c) medulla      d) hair shaft

23. An atom is the smallest chemical part of a/an:

   a) element      b) molecule      c) compound      d) suspension

24. The oxidizing agent added to haircolor or lightener that assists in the development process:

   a) hydrogen peroxide      b) developer      c) catalyst      d) all of the above

25. Gradual dye, also known as a metallic dye, contains:

a) fiber      b) vegetable      **c) metal**      d) oxygen

26. Double process haircolor involves lightening the hair, followed by a:

**a) toner**      b) glazing      c) dark color      d) lighter color

27. A _____ is used to replace any missing primary color(s) in the hair:

a) drabber      b) lightener      **c) filler**      d) intensifier

28. Electrons are the particles in an atom that have a/an:

a) positive charge      **b) negative charge**      c) alternating current      d) direct current

29. Haircolor remover is a solution used to remove existing haircolor with minimal:

a) lift      **b) damage**      c) deposit      d) dye

30. Emulsions are:

a) two immiscible liquids      b) oil and water      **c) both a and b**      d) neither a nor b

31. A _____ is used to add shine to the hair:

a) filler      **b) glaze**      c) temporary      d) none of the above

32. In order to reduce the amount of unwanted warmth in a haircolor, you can use a/an:

a) intensifier      b) filler      **c) drabber**      d) lightener

33. Weaving or slicing are two types of:

a) painting techniques      b) glazing techniques      **c) foiling techniques**      d) corrective color techniques

34. Eumelanin, the most abundant type of human melanin, produces _____ pigments in the hair:

a) red to violet      b) yellow to red      **c) brown to black**      d) yellow to white

35. Stimulates the imagination by allowing you to create arrangements of two or more colors anywhere on the head:

a) painting      b) glazing      c) reverse color      **d) dimensional technique**

36. The simplest form of matter is a/an:

a) atom      b) proton      **c) element**      d) compound

37. Your Guest has haircolor on her skin around the hairline, you will need to use:

   a) hand soap        b) face cream        c) haircolor stain remover        d) haircolor remover

38. A concentrated product that is added to a haircolor formulation to make the end result more vibrant:

   a) intensifier        b) contributing pigment        c) drabber        d) fashion color

39. Hydrogen peroxide is also known as:

   a) developer        b) catalyst        c) oxidizing agent        d) all of the above

40. _____ is classified on the color wheel from warm to cool; also referred to as tone:

   a) Hue        b) Undertone        c) Intensity        d) Level

41. The law of color is a system that helps to provide an understanding of:

   a) color relationships    b) color tones        c) color neutralization        d) all of the above

42. Highlighting is a haircoloring technique that _____ natural or artificial haircolor:

   a) darkens        b) lightens        c) lightens and darkens    d) none of the above

43. Ion / ions are electrically charged _____ formed by the loss or gain of one or more electrons:

   a) matter        b) molecules        c) atoms        d) elements

44. Rocks, water, and minerals do not contain carbon. They are examples used while studying:

   a) natural chemistry    b) compound chemistry    c) organic chemistry    d) inorganic chemistry

45. The degree of lightness or darkness:

   a) texture        b) level        c) porosity        d) form

46. The foiling technique that adds darker pigment to selected strands of hair:

   a) highlighting        b) lowlighting        c) pre-lightening        d) lightening

47. _____ is divided into two basic categories: on the scalp and off the scalp:

   a) Compound dye    b) Indirect dye        c) Aniline derivative color        d) Lightener

48. A visible line or band between two haircolors, artificial and/or natural:

   a) line of separation    b) line of demarcation    c) line of lightening    d) line of color

# HAIRCOLORING
## STATE BOARD THEORY REVIEW

49. The system that categorizes haircolor numerically:

a) color system      b) tonal system      c) level system      d) hue system

50. Metallic dye products contain metals that create a/an_____ build-up of color:

a) slow      b) rapid      c) quick      d) even

51. The innermost layer of hair:

a) cuticle      b) cortex      c) medulla      d) hair strand

52. The coloring matter that provides the natural color to our hair and skin:

a) pigment      b) melanin      c) dye      d) bond

53. Chemistry is the science that deals with the composition, structures, and properties of:

a) matter      b) chemicals      c) haircolor      d) oxygen

54. This type of lightener is available in cream, oil and some powder forms:

a) single lighteners      b) off the scalp lighteners      c) on the scalp lighteners      d) purple lighteners

55. Non-oxidative haircolor does not change the hair chemically and is used to:

a) darken color      b) add subtle tone      c) impart shine      d) all of the above

56. A neutron is a_____ particle with zero electrical charge and a mass equal to that of a proton:

a) positive      b) negative      c) neutral      d) none of the above

57. Hair as it grows out from the scalp that has not been chemically treated:

a) re-touch      b) single process      c) resistant      d) new growth

58. The branch of chemistry that deals with products containing carbon:

a) organic chemistry      b) inorganic chemistry      c) atomic chemistry      d) molecular chemistry

59. Quick lighteners are another name for:

a) single lighteners      b) off the scalp lighteners      c) on the scalp lighteners      d) purple lighteners

60. Molecules are two or more atoms _____ joined, and retain their chemical and physical properties to form matter:

a) physically      b) chemically      c) forcibly      d) electrically

# HAIRCOLORING
## STATE BOARD THEORY REVIEW

61. Natural hair dye is a non-professional haircolor, also known as:

a) vegetable hair dye    b) mineral dye    c) lightening dye    d) none of the above

62. An example of overlapping would be when the haircolor products spread onto:

a) previously colored hair    b) previously lightened hair    c) new growth    d) both a and b

63. A patch test displaying rash, hives, swelling or inflammation has a _____ reaction:

a) positive    b) negative    c) safe    d) general

64. Oxidative haircolor creates a chemical change in the hair, providing _____ haircolor results:

a) longer lasting    b) blending    c) combustion    d) oxidation

65. A chemical reaction in which the oxidizing agent is reduced, and the reducing agent is oxidized:

a) oxidation-reduction    b) redox    c) decolorization    d) both a and b

66. The chemical reaction in which oxygen is added to an element or compound:

a) pre-softening    b) blending    c) combustion    d) oxidation

67. Potential hydrogen (pH) is the concentrated amount of hydrogen ions in a solution containing:

a) salt    b) oxygen    c) water    d) ammonia

68. Pheomelanin produces _____ pigments in the hair:

a) red to violet    b) yellow to red    c) orange to brown    d) brown to black

69. Pigment is what gives color its color; its source can be natural, mineral or:

a) physical    b) chemical    c) both a and b    d) neither a nor b

70. The strongest category of haircolor that can deposit and lighten natural pigments:

a) semi-permanent    b) demi-permanent    c) permanent    d) decolorizers

71. Primary colors consist of:

a) red, green, orange    b) red, yellow, green    c) red, green, blue    d) red, yellow, blue

72. Diffusing or lifting the natural hair color to achieve the desired end result:

a) lowlighting    b) pre-lightening    c) dyeing    d) haircoloring

73. Increasing the porosity of the hair by opening the cuticle and allowing for more pigment to be absorbed:

a) pre-toning     b) pre-lightening     c) pre-softening     d) pre-coloring

74. A 24 to 48 hour test to check for sensitivity and/or allergic reaction:

a) strand     b) oxidation     c) predisposition     d) hair

75. Redox is also known as:

a) combustion     b) peroxide     c) developer     d) oxidation-reduction

76. Protons are particles in an atom that have a:

a) positive charge     b) negative charge     c) neutral charge     d) none of the above

77. _____ have definite chemical and physical properties:

a) Solvents     b) Ammonia     c) Concentrates     d) Pure substances

78. A test performed during a haircolor service to determine the progression of the haircolor:

a) processing strand     b) patch     c) elasticity     d) porosity

79. Reverse highlighting is also known as:

a) highlighting     b) lowlighting     c) double process     d) corrective haircoloring

80. Mixing red and blue in equal proportions creates a:

a) primary color     b) secondary color     c) tertiary color     d) complementary color

81. Reverse haircolor is also known as:

a) return color     b) tint back     c) filler     d) none of the above

82. The flatter the cuticle scales, the more _____ the hair:

a) porous     b) absorbent     c) accessible     d) resistant

83. Semi-permanent haircolor that penetrates the cuticle layer will gradually fade depending on:

a) haircolor formulation     b) the application process     c) the density     d) how often hair is shampooed

84. Water is an example of a/an:

a) ointment     b) solvent     c) both a and b     d) neither a nor b

# HAIRCOLORING
## STATE BOARD THEORY REVIEW

85. Solutions are stable mixtures of two or more:

    a) solids          b) liquids          c) gases          d) all of the above

86. A haircoloring process that can lighten and deposit color in one step:

    a) triple process    b) double process    c) single process    d) none of the above

87. Special effects are techniques used to create:

    a) highlights       b) lowlights        c) dimension        d) all of the above

88. When natural hair color is diffused from the hair, the hair goes through a process called the:

    a) levels of          b) stages of          c) stages of          d) levels of removal
       coloration            decolorization        pigmentation

89. The process of returning hair back to its natural state or desired level / color:

    a) reverse color    b) tint back        c) both a and b     d) neither a or b

90. Virgin haircolor application implies the hair has been colored how many times:

    a) 0                b) 1                c) 2                d) multiple

91. Mixing red and violet creates a _____ color:

    a) primary          b) secondary        c) tertiary         d) complementary

92. The particles of a/an _____ are likely to settle and separate:

    a) solution         b) suspension       c) ointment         d) soap

93. Henna is an example of:

    a) permanent hair dye  b) vegetable hair dye   c) indirect hair dye   d) direct hair dye

94. After decolorizing the hair, toners are typically used to:

    a) neutralize       b) cleanse          c) lighten          d) all of the above

95. Undertone is the warm or cool tones seen within the predominant haircolor that are the result of _____ pigment found in the hair:

    a) artificial       b) natural          c) direct           d) indirect

96. Natural cool tones are:

    a) red and yellow   b) red and orange   c) blue and yellow  d) blue and violet

97. Color tinted shampoo is categorized as _____ haircolor:

    a) temporary        b) semi-permanent   c) demi-permanent   d) permanent

98. The level of concentration and strength of hydrogen peroxide:

    a) level            b) regulator        c) concentrator     d) volume

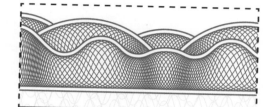

NT OF STA

& OCCUPATIONAL

State 12345

gy License

E NAME
STREET
TE 12345

# CHEMICAL
# TEXTURIZING

Chemical Texturizing

1. _disinfecting_ *Pg. 387* cleaning tools with warm, soapy water and submerging in an EPA-registered disinfectant

2. _draping_ *Pg. 340* used to protect Guests' clothing and skin against chemicals and/or irritation

3. _GHS_ *Pg. 388* sets the standards for what information the SDS contains

4. _Occupational Disease_ *Pg. 388* a disease that is caused by overexposure to certain products or ingredients

5. _OSHA_ *Pg. 388* mandates that every chemical located within a business has a SDS available

6. _____ strand tests are to be performed before every chemical service to determine processing time

7. _____ a form affirming that your Guest was advised of potential risks associated with a chemical service

8. _____ cleaning tools with warm soapy water to remove all debris and then placing them in a high pressure steam unit

# SAFETY AND DISINFECTION

## WORD SEARCH

| | | | | | | | | | | | | | | |
|---|---|---|---|---|---|---|---|---|---|---|---|---|---|---|
| G | N | I | T | C | E | F | N | I | S | I | D | S | Y | R |
| L | K | A | K | M | W | M | V | E | H | U | T | O | R | E |
| S | A | O | G | N | X | K | S | L | J | E | O | R | A | L |
| T | B | N | T | R | G | X | M | Z | R | G | R | M | N | E |
| E | L | Q | O | X | M | S | H | I | N | J | R | I | I | A |
| G | L | L | I | I | P | V | L | I | Z | D | G | S | M | S |
| Z | H | J | V | J | T | I | P | G | J | N | P | Q | I | E |
| J | I | S | X | G | Z | A | S | V | K | K | R | W | L | S |
| D | K | L | T | A | R | A | P | M | K | S | R | W | E | T |
| U | U | Q | T | D | Y | C | Z | U | O | S | H | A | R | A |
| Y | C | I | E | F | M | Y | R | X | C | Y | E | I | P | T |
| M | O | E | M | I | V | S | Q | B | H | C | M | A | B | E |
| N | J | P | R | L | Q | H | O | F | I | J | O | D | G | M |
| F | P | A | O | G | B | I | V | C | V | F | R | D | F | E |
| B | C | E | O | D | D | V | X | N | V | L | D | V | X | N |
| M | Y | Q | I | E | R | W | Z | P | O | O | S | J | H | T |

# COMPOSITION OF THE HAIR

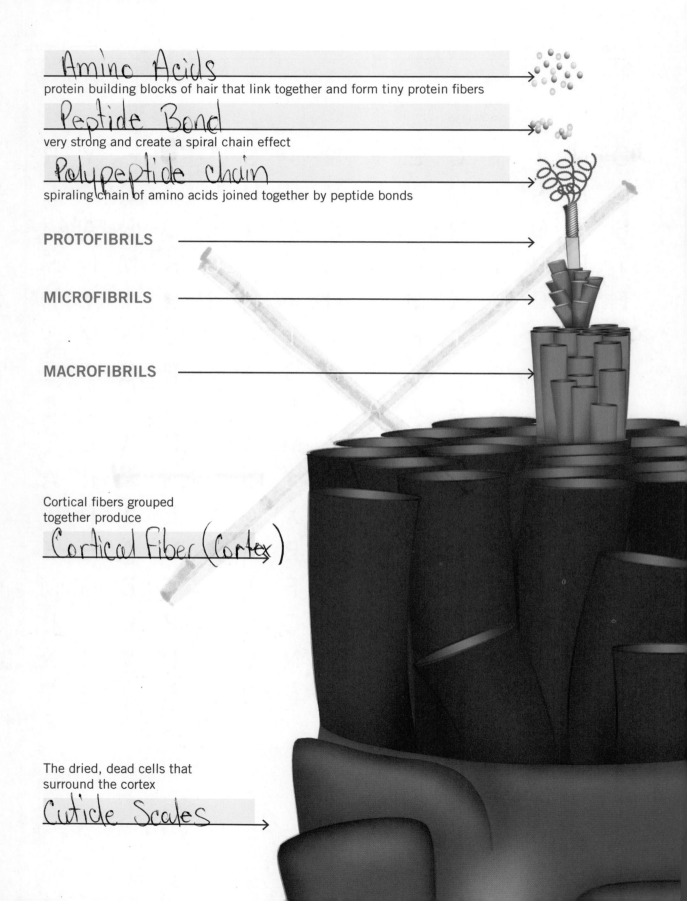

_Amino Acids_

protein building blocks of hair that link together and form tiny protein fibers

_Peptide Bond_

very strong and create a spiral chain effect

_Polypeptide chain_

spiraling chain of amino acids joined together by peptide bonds

**PROTOFIBRILS**

**MICROFIBRILS**

**MACROFIBRILS**

Cortical fibers grouped together produce

_Cortical Fiber (cortex)_

The dried, dead cells that surround the cortex

_Cuticle Scales_

# BONDS OF THE HAIR

Like the steps on a ladder, _____ _____ connect polypeptide chains side-by-side and are responsible for the hair's strength and elasticity.

## TYPES OF SIDE BONDS

| TYPE | STRENGTH | BROKEN BY | REFORMED BY |
|---|---|---|---|
| Hydrogen | weak | water/heat | when hair cools/dries |
| Salt | weak | changes in PH | when pH is restored |
| Disulfide | strong | chemical solution | neutralizing or cutting |

## PHYSICAL AND CHEMICAL CHANGES TO THE HAIR

Describe what happens to hair when it is temporarily altered:

Wet, flexible, managable hair is stretched when wrapped around perm rods. Then dry hair completely and cool, then remove rods/rollers.

Describe what happens to hair when it is permanently altered:

double process. first physical/temporary change process, second chemical applied while wet the dried to create new curly form

STRAIGHT, DRY HAIR; HYDROGEN BONDS ARE INTACT

HAIR IS WET; HYDROGEN BONDS DETACH

WET HAIR IS STRETCHED AROUND ROLLER

WHEN HAIR IS DRY; HYDROGEN BONDS RE-ATTACH IN NEW POSITION

# MIXTURES IN CHEMISTRY

## 3 FORMS OF MATTER

Consists of molecules that are very far apart

1. _Gas_

**Examples:**

_____

_____

_____

Consists of molecules that are very close together

2. _Liquid_

**Examples:**

_____

_____

_____

Consists of molecules that are the closest together

3. _Solid_

**Examples:**

_____

_____

_____

A physical combination of 2 or more types of matter blended together is _physical_ _mixtures_ .

When one substance is able to be mixed with another substance to form a stable substance, they are called _____ .

## Give examples of each type of substance:

| MISCIBLE | IMMISCIBLE |
|---|---|
| Alcohol | |
| water | |
| | |

# MEASURES OF pH Pg. 401

The measurement of hydrogen ions in a solution to determine its acidity or alkalinity is called Potential Hydrogen, or abbreviated as pH. A pH scale is logarithmically designed to measure if a product is acidic, neutral, or alkaline.

**Test products that you will be using in this chapter, and list them on the scale next to their corresponding number.**

Acidic
products contract and harden the hair.

| 0 |
| 1 |
| 2 |
| 3 |
| 4 |
| 5 |
| 6 |
| 7 |
| 8 |
| 9 |
| 10 |
| 11 |
| 12 |
| 13 |
| 14 |

Alkaline
products soften and swell the hair.

# PERMANENT WAVING

**What is Permanent Waving?**

chemical change to hair making straight hair into a curly or wavy form.

## THE THREE PHASES OF A PERMANENT WAVE PROCESS:

1. _processing_ requires applying a permanent waving lotion to hair that has been wrapped.

2. _Neutralizing_ requires the application of a chemical solution to stop the waving process.

_Neutralizer_ is the chemical solution applied to stop the waving process and to rebuild the bonds into their new form.

_Thio Neutralization_ is the complete process.

3. _Preliminary_ _Test_ _Curl_ determines the required processing time and ensures that the desired curl has been achieved.

_over_ - _processed_ causes dry, damaged hair with increased breakage.

_Under_ - _processed_ causes insufficient curl pattern due to timing or inadequate saturation.

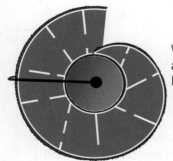

Waving lotion is applied, disulfide bonds separate.

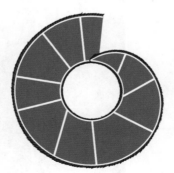

Neutralizer reforms disulfide bonds in their new curled position, perm rod is removed.

In your own words, explain the processes of **reduction** and **oxidation**:

reduction-

# PERM CATEGORIES pg. 405

| PERM TYPE | RECOMMENDED HAIR TYPE | PROCESSING (HEAT / NO HEAT) | ACTIVE INGREDIENT | pH |
|---|---|---|---|---|
| (A.K.A COLD WAVES) | Alkaline waves | no heat | | |
| | Porous, fragile, color-treated, damaged | | | 4.5 to 7.0 |
| | | | typically Glyceryl Monothioglycolate (GMTG) | |
| | | no heat | Glyceryl Monothioglycolate (GMTG) | |
| ENDOTHERMIC | | | | 4.5 to 7.5 |
| | Coarse, resistant, extremely thick | | Ammonium Thioglycolate | |
| AMMONIA-FREE | | no heat | Monoethanolamine (MEA) / Aminomethylpropanol (AMP) | |
| THIO-FREE | | | Mercaptamine / Cysteamine | |
| LOW pH | | with heat | Ammonium Sulfate / Ammonium Bisulfate | 6.5 to 7.0 |

# PERM TOOLS AND TECHNIQUES | CROSSWORD PUZZLE

## DOWN

1. wrap technique using controlled sections of hair in which perm rods are placed in rectangular sections

2. wrap technique that utilizes two rods, one rod wrapped mid-strand to scalp, one rod wrapped mid-strand to ends

4. wrap technique used on hair longer than 8" to provide a uniform pattern from scalp to ends

8. wrap technique that consists of multiple small ponytails throughout the head, each wrapped with 5 to 7 rods

9. wrap that requires one paper placed on top of remaining exposed hair, ensuring all hair is wrapped smoothly around the rod

10. perm rods that are foam covered and easily bent

12. wrap technique that creates a coiling, springing effect on the hair

13. wrap technique that consists of partings that follow the shape of the head

14. wrap technique that has no exact sections, rods are staggered

15. perm rods that are pliable foam and create a soft-end result

16. wrap technique that produces curls that are tighter on the ends and larger at the scalp

17. wrap technique that consists of controlled sections of hair using zigzag partings

20. wrap that requires only one paper, which is folded in half

## ACROSS

3. absorbent pieces of thin tissue-type paper that control and protect the hair ends while perming

5. wrapping technique that provides curl or wave to small areas of the head

6. perm rods that have an even diameter and width throughout their entire length

7. used to maintain balance and eliminate pressure by lifting the bands of perm rods off the hair

11. the position of a perm rod within a section

18. perm rods that have a small diameter in the center with a larger diameter increase throughout the remaining length

19. wrap that requires hair to be placed between two end papers

21. perm rods that are long and plastic; wrapped straight, then bent and connected to form a circle

22. subsections located within a larger section

23. position of a tool in relation to its base section and is determined by the angle at which the hair is wrapped

# PERM TOOLS AND TECHNIQUES | CROSSWORD PUZZLE

# TESTING THE HAIR

When performing chemical services on your Guest's hair, you will need to perform a simple, but necessary test to determine if the hair is healthy or in need of some TLC (tender loving care).

**The ability of the hair to absorb any liquid is _____.**

**Fill in the blanks and describe the three types of porosity.**

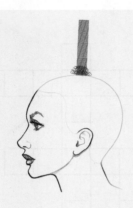  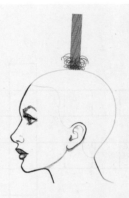

_____    _____    _____

**POROSITY**                **POROSITY**                **POROSITY**

**The capability of the hair strand to stretch and return to its previous form without breaking is _____.**

Wet hair can generally be stretched on average _____% of its length.

Dry hair can generally be stretched on average _____% of its length.

**Describe each step of an elasticity test:**

_____    _____    _____

_____    _____    _____

# CHEMICAL STRAIGHTENING pg. 446

**What is Chemical Relaxing?**

to chemically alter naturally curly or wavy hair into a straighter form

## CURL REDUCTION pg. 447

**Determine the percentage of curl relaxation and fill in the blank under each.**

| _0_ % | _25_ % | _50_ % | _75_ % | _100_ % |
|---|---|---|---|---|
| no relaxation | moderate relaxation | average relaxation | optimum relaxation | maximum relaxation |

## TWO PHASES OF A CHEMICAL RELAXING PROCESS: Pg. 448, 450

1. _____ _____ is the application of a chemical agent to the hair, followed by a series of steps necessary to straighten the hair.

   __Base__ __Cream__ is used as a barrier to protect the scalp and is applied prior to a chemical relaxer service.

2. _Neutralizing_ requires applying a chemical that reconnects the disulfide bonds for thio relaxers or restores the pH back to normal when using hydroxide relaxers.

   _Rebonding_ chemically restores the disulfide bonds to their newly hardened shape.

   ~~Hydroxide Neutralization~~ this process neutralizes any remaining alkaline residue left by a hydroxide relaxer and helps to restore the pH of the hair and scalp.

# CHEMICAL RELAXERS Q

pg. 451

## STRENGTHS

**Super**
best used on coarse textured hair with resistant porosity

**Regular**
typically used on medium textured hair with normal porosity

**Mild**
best used on color treated, fine textured hair with severe porosity

## TYPES

**Thioglycolate Relaxers**
are chemical compounds with the additive ingredient ammonia; process in the same manner as a perm; have a low pH

**Hydroxide Relaxers**
have a high alkaline content; available in varying formulas; strongest relaxer with an alkaline pH above 12

## FORMS

## CATEGORIES

### SODIUM / LYE

**pH:** 12.5-13.5

**Use on:** curly resistant course texture

### POTASSIUM / LITHIUM / NO-LYE

**pH:** 12.5-13.5

**Use on:** Medium textures

### METAL HYDROXIDE

**pH:** 12.5-13.5

**Use on:** _____

### GUANIDINE

**pH:** 10-13

**Use on:** _____

## CATEGORIES

### AMMONIUM THIOGLYCOLATE

**pH:** 9.6-10

**Use on:** less resistant fine to medium texture

### AMMONIUM BISULFITE

**pH:** 6.5-8.5

**Use on:** _____

## NEUTRALIZATION

_____ is the process of removing 1 sulfur atom and replacing it with a disulfide bond.

Normalizing lotions are:
_____
_____
_____

Neutralizing shampoos help to:
_____
_____
_____

# CHEMICAL SMOOTHING

A texture service that restructures overly curly hair into loose curls or waves is _____.

A texture service that helps to eliminate frizz, curl and improve manageability by depositing a strong, fibrous protein is _____  _____.

## COMMON COMPONENTS OF KERATIN SMOOTHING TREATMENTS

Formaldehyde is:

_____

_____

Formaldehyde Free is:

_____

_____

_____

results from the oxidation of primary alcohols

## BEST PRACTICES OF CHEMICAL SMOOTHING:

1.

2.

3.

4.

5.

# HEAD DIAGRAM

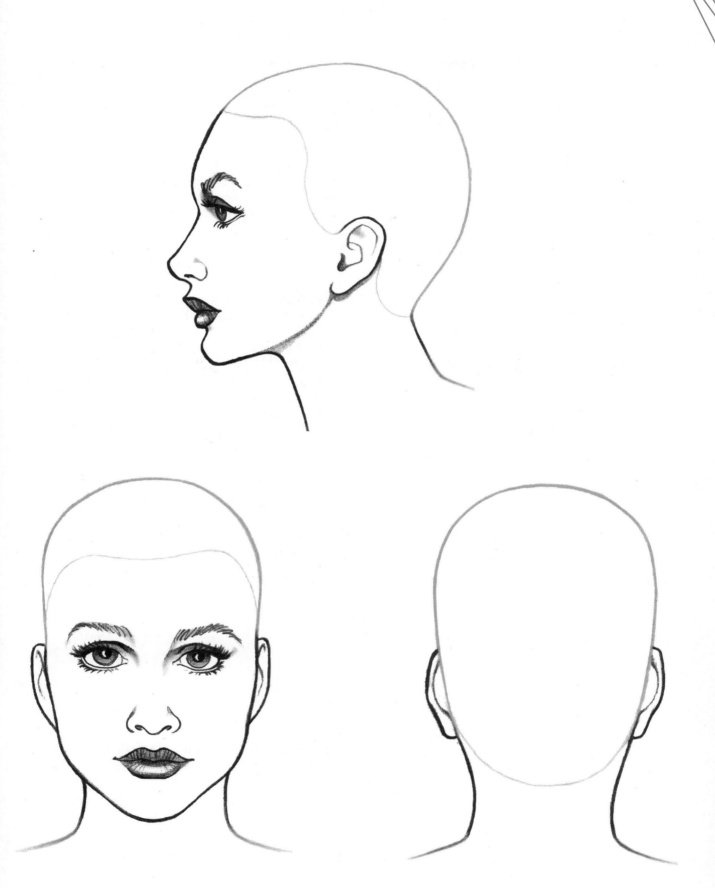

# DEVELOPING YOUR CHEMICAL TEXTURIZING COMMUNICATION AND SOLUTION SKILLS

What consultation question(s) would you have prepared to ask your Guest for the following:

Permanent Waving:_____

Relaxer:_____

Keratin Smoothing:_____

_____

Your Guest informs you that they would like to completely remove all curl from their hair.
What straightening service would you use for the following hair types and why?

Fine:_____

Medium:_____

Coarse:_____

Your Guest states that they would like to change their haircolor after having a straightening service.
How would you respond and proceed?

_____

_____

Your Guest tells you that they experienced some scalp and/or skin irritation after their last service.
Given this information, how would you respond and proceed?

_____

_____

## SERVICE RECOMMENDATIONS

What styling recommendations will you discuss with your Guest for:

Permanent Waving:_____

Relaxer:_____

Keratin Smoothing:_____

## MAINTENANCE RECOMMENDATIONS

When discussing a maintenance routine with your Guest, how often will you suggest they rebook for the following?

Permanent Waving:_____

Relaxer:_____

Keratin Smoothing:_____

## PRODUCT RECOMMENDATIONS

What product recommendations will you discuss with your Guest and why?

_____

_____

Shampoo:_____

Conditioner:_____

Styling:_____

Finishing:_____

# SITUATIONAL SCENARIOS

**1.** Throughout the service, your Guest expressed concerns regarding the condition of their hair after the chemical service. How should you address their concern?

    **a)** Chemicals do not cause any damage to the hair, so there is no need for concern
    **b)** Suggest various shine products that will camouflage any damage
    **c)** To alleviate any damage, suggest reconstructing conditioners to help repair their hair
    **d)** Recommend a new haircolor and haircut to draw the attention away from the damaged hair

**2.** During the chemical straightening process, your Guest begins to feel a burning in the nape area. You have just started applying the relaxer and have two additional sections to complete. What action should be taken to assist in reducing the burning?

    **a)** Apply a piece of cotton saturated with neutralizer to the sensitive area
    **b)** Immediately stop the application and rinse it from the head
    **c)** Continue with application and explain they will need to deal with the burning since you are done applying the relaxer
    **d)** Wipe the sensitive area and apply additional base cream

**3.** Tonya requests a perm wrap technique that will make her one-length hair have uniform curl from the scalp to the ends. What type of perm wrap technique will you recommend to achieve the final results?

    **a)** Croquignole wrap
    **b)** Bricklay wrap
    **c)** Spiral wrap
    **d)** Weave wrap

**4.** After a permanent wave service on your new Guest, you notice that the curl pattern appears weak and limp. What could have been the cause of this problem?

    **a)** Under-processing; test curl done incorrectly
    **b)** Perm processed too long
    **c)** Vigorous shampoo prior to the perm
    **d)** Poorly conditioned hair

**5.** During a scalp and hair analysis for a permanent wave, you notice that your Guest has a severe case of eczema in the nape that appears to be infected, scaly and bleeding. How should you proceed?

    **a)** Inform your Guest of the scalp situation and proceed with the service
    **b)** Ignore the problem and continue with the service
    **c)** Explain to your Guest that you will not be able to proceed with the permanent wave service and recommend they see a medical professional
    **d)** Reschedule the perm service in two days and recommend the proper ointment to clear the problem

**6.** To achieve the best results, what perm should be recommended to a perm Guest who recently began receiving haircolor services?

    **a)** Cold wave
    **b)** Acid wave
    **c)** Ammonium thioglycolate wave
    **d)** Ammonia-free wave

**7.** During a consultation, Kelly reveals that she is having a difficult time maintaining the style of her newly layered 3 inch haircut. Her hair lacks fullness and movement. You recommend a body wave. What color and/or size rods would you use to achieve the desired wave pattern?

    **a)** Red
    **b)** Blue
    **c)** Purple
    **d)** Brown

**8.** When performing your Guest's scalp and hair analysis, you notice hair breakage in the back of their head. As you proceed with the consultation, your Guest states that they have never had a chemical relaxer done professionally in the salon. What are some precautionary measures you should take prior to the chemical relaxer?

    **a)** Test a strand of hair every three minutes or as directed by manufacturer
    **b)** Do not overlap the relaxer during application
    **c)** Choose the correct strength of relaxer based on the texture and porosity
    **d)** All of the above

**9.** Your 2:00 pm appointment is a new Guest scheduled for a soft curl reformation. During the hair and scalp analysis, you notice that 2 inches of her hair has some type of chemical straightening process. When you question your Guest, she explains that her last relaxer was done 6 months ago. How should you proceed to achieve the best results?

    **a)** Explain to your Guest that the two chemical processes cannot be combined. To achieve the proper results, the 2 inches of chemically straightened hair will need to be removed before receiving the service
    **b)** Explain to your Guest that she will need to grow her hair for another 6 months before even considering the soft curl reformation
    **c)** Proceed with the soft curl reformation service and the ends will curl
    **d)** Under no circumstances can the service be preformed; explain to the Guest they will never be able to receive the service

**10.** Mrs. Smith, a new Guest, wants her layered hair straight. During the consultation Mrs. Smith reveals that her past relaxers caused scalp irritation. What type of relaxer should be used on Mrs. Smith to assist in avoiding scalp irritation?

    **a)** Sodium hydroxide
    **b)** Lithium hydroxide
    **c)** Potassium hydroxide
    **d)** Guanidine hydroxide

**11.** Charlotte requested a straightening service that will help to eliminate the frizz and improve the manageability of her hair. She does not want to commit to the new style for more than 10 to 12 weeks. What procedure would you recommend to Charlotte?

    **a)** Sodium hydroxide relaxer
    **b)** Ammonium thioglycolate relaxer
    **c)** Keratin smoothing treatment
    **d)** Japanese thermal straightener

**12.** Felicia, your 5:00 pm permanent wave appointment calls to say she is running late. It is taking her longer to get to the salon from her new house. During the consultation, she states that recently her hair has been slightly drier and stiff.

    **a)** Inform your assistant to use a moisturizing shampoo on her
    **b)** The new house could have well water, complete a clarifying treatment to remove any mineral deposits on the hair
    **c)** Felicia's hair does not feel dry, so just ignore the problem
    **d)** Reschedule Felicia's permanent wave appointment and give Felicia a conditioning treatment today, especially since she is late

# WORKSHOP
# standards

## Safety and Infection Control:

Disinfect work station *(before and after each service)*
Set up work station with required, clean service tools

## Consultation:

Scalp Analysis:   □oily   □normal   □dry   □abrasions
Hair Analysis:   □density   □texture   □elasticity   □porosity
Drape: neck strip, towel, cape, towel

## Shampoo Bowl Safety:

Maintain control of nozzle at all times, with constant temperature check
Gently cleanse scalp and hair *(if applicable)*
Disinfect shampoo bowl and water nozzle

## Permanent Wave: *9-Block Basic Perm Wrap*

Application of perm rods:   □on-base   □off-base   □half off-base
Neatly apply protective cream and cotton around hairline and ears
Apply waving lotion to top and bottom of perm rod along full length of rod; then apply lotion to middle of perm rods
Remove saturated cotton; replace with new cotton
Apply processing cap; process according to manufacturer's directions
Test Curl – check for 'S' shaping
When processing is complete, remove cap and cotton; continue to 'Finishing of Service'

## Relaxer: *Virgin Application*

Apply gloves
Section into 4 quadrants
Part hair into ¼" to ½" subsections, applying base to entire scalp (including hairline and ears)
Starting at most resistant area – part hair into ¼" subsections
Apply relaxer to most resistant area, staying ½" away from scalp
Continue applying relaxer using ¼" subsections, staying 1" away from ends, covering both sides of subsection
Starting at nape area, part hair into 1" subsections
Using a tail comb or spine of comb, smooth hair, applying slight firm pressure; continue to smooth all sections
Process according to manufacturer's directions
Perform curl relaxation strand test

## Finishing of Service:

Rinse hair thoroughly for a minimum of 5 minutes
Towel blot; apply neutralizing product; process according to manufacturer's directions
   **Perm:** Remove rods without tension; rinse
   **Relaxer:** Apply a conditioner, comb through; rinse
Complete style as desired
Recommend at-home maintenance product(s)

# practical PREP

*Each skill will be checked by your Educator and feedback will be provided.*
*Perm and Relaxer are mock applications.*
*Met Skill = 1 point / Not Met Skill = 0 points*

**POINTS**

## Safety and Disinfection:

Disinfects work station *(before and after each service)*
Station set up with required tools
Drapes for a chemical service
Performs scalp and hair analysis
Neatly divides and clips hair into appropriate number of sections
Applies protective gloves
Applies protective cream around hairline and ears
**Feedback:**

## Permanent Waving *(one quadrant):*

Section width correlates with length of rod
Subsection correlates with diameter of rod size
Extends end papers beyond hair ends
Wraps hair evenly and smoothly around rod
Wraps hair around rod at least 1½ times
Places bands correctly
Demonstrates a test curl
Finishes without fish hooks
**Feedback:**

## Chemical Relaxer – Virgin Application *(one quadrant):*

Uses ¼" partings
Application and control of relaxer to mid-shaft only *(neatly applies around hairline, no dripping, staying ¼" away from scalp and up to ½" away from ends)*
Applies product to scalp area and ends
Smooths hair with back of non-metal comb, fingers or applicator brush
Cross-checks sections to ensure complete coverage
**Feedback:**

## Chemical Relaxer – Retouch *(one quadrant):*

Uses ⅛" partings
Applies product to re-growth only with no overlap
Smooths hair with back of non-metal comb, fingers or applicator brush
Cross-checks sections to ensure complete coverage
Keeps mid-shaft and ends free from product
**Feedback:**

Chemical Texturizing

155

# CHEMICAL TEXTURIZING
## STATE BOARD THEORY REVIEW

1. 9-block wrap is also known as:

   a) spiral wrap     b) bricklay wrap     c) basic permanent wrap     d) general permanent wrap

2. The oxidation of primary _____ creates aldehyde:

   a) alcohols     b) ammonium     c) sodium hydroxide     d) hydrogen peroxide

3. The chemical solution that stops the waving process of a permanent wave and rebuilds the bonds into their new form:

   a) water     b) ammonia     c) neutralizer     d) keratin

4. Waves that require no heat and have a pH above 7.1 are:

   a) acid     b) neutral     c) alkaline     d) free waves

5. A mild, alternative relaxer that contains a low pH and is compatible with thio relaxers:

   a) keratin     b) guanidine hydroxide     c) lithium hydroxide     d) ammonium bilsulfite relaxer

6. Chemical relaxing is to alter naturally curly or wavy hair into a _____ form:

   a) round     b) straighter     c) coiled     d) over curly

7. The main ingredient in an alkaline wave:

   a) thioglycolic acid     b) sodium hydroxide     c) glyceryl monothioglycolate     d) hydrogen peroxide

8. The position of the perm rod within the section:

   a) base control     b) base placement     c) base direction     d) both a and b

9. Used as a barrier to protect the scalp from chemicals during a relaxer:

   a) hair lotion     b) neutralizing lotion     c) base cream     d) face cream

10. _____ waves use an ingredient to reduce the odor associated with perms:

   a) Sodium     b) Alkaline     c) Keratin     d) Ammonia-free

11. A _____ requires a protective base cream to be applied:

a) base relaxer
b) retouch relaxer
c) virgin relaxer
d) none of the above

12. Double-rod wrap is also known as:

a) rod on rod wrap
b) partial wrap
c) stacked wrap
d) piggyback wrap

13. Base placement is also known as:

a) base control
b) base size
c) base movement
d) base direction

14. A flexible, foam covered rod:

a) straight rod
b) concave rod
c) bender rod
d) spiral rod

15. An end wrap technique with one folded paper:

a) book end
b) single
c) double
d) flat

16. The layer of the hair that contains melanin:

a) cuticle
b) cortex
c) medulla
d) hair shaft

17. A staggered wrapping pattern:

a) cushion wrap
b) bricklay perm wrap
c) spiral wrap
d) book end wrap

18. Rods that have a small diameter in the center and a larger diameter throughout the length:

a) concave
b) straight
c) loop
d) spiral

19. Disulfide bonds connect two sulfur atoms located in the amino acid called:

a) peptide
b) keratin
c) cysteine
d) amino

20. Cold waves are also known as:

a) acid waves
b) alkaline waves
c) glyceryl monothioglycolate
d) hydroxide waves

21. Cross bonds are also known as:

a) side bonds
b) physical bonds
c) chemical bonds
d) hydroxide bonds

22. A perm wrap that consists of partings that follow the shape of the head:

   a) oblong          b) triangle          c) curvature          d) rectangle

23. A _____ is formed from two or more substances combined but not chemically changed:

   a) suspension      b) physical mixture  c) solution          d) composition

24. _____ uses two end papers, one on each side of the hair strand:

   a) Single flat wrap  b) Triple flat wrap  c) Double flat wrap  d) Book wrap

25. These bonds can only be broken with chemical solutions:

   a) physical bonds  b) disulfide bonds   c) side bonds        d) salt bonds

26. _____ are proteins that link together to form tiny fibers:

   a) Amino acids     b) Atoms             c) Calciums          d) Carbons

27. The capability of the hair strand to stretch and return to its previous form without breaking:

   a) texture         b) density           c) elasticity        d) porosity

28. End bonds are also known as:

   a) side bonds      b) physical bonds    c) acid bonds        d) peptide bonds

29. A perm that is self-heating:

   a) alkaline perm   b) reducing agent    c) exothermic        d) endothermic

30. This permanent wave processes without heat, produces a firmer curl, and has a pH between 7.0 to 8.2:

   a) thio-free       b) acid balanced     c) ammonia           d) endothermic

31. End papers are _____ pieces of thin tissue-type paper:

   a) impermeable     b) nonporous         c) absorbent         d) waterproof

32. The process of removing one sulfur atom and replacing it with a disulfide bond is:

   a) neutralization  b) hydrogenization   c) keratinization    d) lanthionization

33. An organic compound that is a colorless, flammable and pungent gas:

   a) formaldehyde   b) formaldehyde free   c) aldehyde   d) none of the above

34. Derived from glycerin, _____ is an odorless, colorless liquid that is miscible in water:

   a) ammonia   b) glyceryl   c) lye   d) sodium

35. A perm that is activated by an outside heat source:

   a) alkaline perm   b) reducing agent   c) exothermic   d) endothermic

36. A wrap technique used to achieve even curl for hair lengths longer than 10 to 12 inches:

   a) root   b) piggyback   c) cushion   d) curvature

37. The main ingredient in a true acid wave:

   a) glyceryl monothioglycolate   b) sodium hydroxide   c) ammonium thioglycolate   d) hydrogen peroxide

38. Type of relaxer that is advertised as no-lye for sensitive skin, and has a slightly lower pH:

   a) sodium hydroxide   b) lithium hydroxide   c) guanidine hydroxide   d) potassium hydroxide

39. Mixing oil and water creates an example of a/an _____ substance:

   a) miscible   b) immiscible   c) catalyst   d) activator

40. Glycerin is an ingredient used in permanent waving lotion to help:

   a) normalize the pH   b) raise the pH   c) lower the pH   d) stabilize the pH

41. Bonds broken by water or heat:

   a) hydrogen bond   b) peptide bond   c) side bond   d) salt bond

42. Wrapping the hair from ends to scalp in overlapping concentric layers:

   a) root   b) spiral   c) partial   d) croquignole

43. Sodium hydroxide relaxers have _____ alkaline content:

   a) slow   b) average   c) low   d) high

# CHEMICAL TEXTURIZING
## STATE BOARD THEORY REVIEW

44. Another name for acid / alkali neutralization reaction is:

   a) thio neutralization
   b) hydroxide neutralization
   c) normalizing neutralization
   d) none of the above

45. In a physical change, matter is altered to a different shape:

   a) temporarily
   b) permanently
   c) continuously
   d) none of the above

46. Keratin is the building block for:

   a) hair
   b) skin
   c) nails
   d) all of the above

47. Lithium hydroxide, a very strong alkaline ingredient used in chemical relaxers, is typically marketed as:

   a) lye, no mixing
   b) no-lye, mixing
   c) no-lye, no-mix
   d) lye, mixing

48. A long, plastic rod used to create spiral curls is known as a circle rod or:

   a) loop rod
   b) flat rod
   c) spiral rod
   d) sponge rod

49. Neutralizing shampoos help to remove any chemicals remaining in the hair and restore the:

   a) color
   b) pH
   c) curl
   d) atoms

50. A metal hydroxide relaxer contains _____ component(s), requiring no mixing:

   a) 1
   b) 2
   c) 3
   d) 4

51. Partial perm wrap is a perming technique that provides curl or wave to:

   a) the entire head
   b) a soft curl pattern
   c) small areas of the head
   d) large areas of the head

52. 'Miscible' means substances:

   a) can mix
   b) cannot mix
   c) require a solution to remain mixed
   d) require heat to be mixed

53. New hair growing out from the scalp that has not been chemically treated:

   a) damaged hair
   b) chemical hair
   c) new growth
   d) fresh hair

# CHEMICAL TEXTURIZING
## STATE BOARD THEORY REVIEW

54. Normalizing lotions are conditioners with _____ pH that restore the hair after a hydroxide relaxer:

   a) neutral        b) acidic        c) alkaline        d) none of the above

55. An inorganic compound that is a colorless, flammable and pungent gas:

   a) ammonia        b) lye        c) formaldehyde        d) sodium

56. A no-base relaxer that does not require a base cream:

   a) lye relaxer        b) sodium relaxer        c) virgin relaxer        d) no-lye relaxer

57. These bonds are connected by amino acids that form polypeptide chains:

   a) physical bonds        b) peptide bonds        c) side bonds        d) salt bonds

58. An occupational disease is any illness caused by _____ to certain products or ingredients:

   a) overexposure        b) underexposure        c) incorrect utilization        d) none of the above

59. Softening or loosening of overly curly hair is known as a:

   a) permanent wave        b) hard press        c) soft curl reformation        d) none of the above

60. Permanent waving permanently rearranges straight hair into _____ pattern:

   a) a curly / wavy        b) a straight        c) a relaxed        d) none of the above

61. The pH scale ranges from:

   a) 0 to 15        b) 1 to 15        c) 0 to 14        d) 1 to 14

62. _____ do not have a chemical reaction:

   a) Chemical properties    b) Physical properties        c) Chemical change        d) Physical alternation

63. This wrap technique produces curl or wave only on the hair ends:

   a) spiral        b) piggyback        c) ponytail        d) weave

64. The ability of hair to absorb any liquid:

   a) texture        b) density        c) elasticity        d) porosity

# CHEMICAL TEXTURIZING
## STATE BOARD THEORY REVIEW

65. Prior to a chemical service, this test is performed to determine how the hair will respond to the chemical:

a) preliminary skin          b) preliminary strand          c) preliminary color          d) preliminary patch

66. True acid waves are permanent waves processed with the application of heat that process _____ than alkaline waves:

a) slower          b) faster          c) the same as          d) longer

67. A _____ is applied around the hairline and ears to protect the skin from permanent wave lotions:

a) protective cream          b) clarifying cream          c) moisturizing cream          d) none of the above

68. The measurement of the acidity or alkalinity of a solution is the:

a) thio          b) pH - potential hydrogen          c) electrons          d) amino acid

69. Chemically restoring the disulfide bonds to their newly hardened shape, also known as rebonding:

a) oxidation          b) processing          c) neutralizing          d) softening

70. A _____ statement is a form affirming that your Guest was advised of any potential risks:

a) patch test          b) consultation          c) record card          d) release

71. _____ bonds are easily broken by a change in pH and reform when the pH balance is restored:

a) Peptide          b) Salt          c) Side          d) Disulfide

72. Reduction is the process through which disulfide bonds are:

a) hardened          b) tightened          c) broken          d) reformed

73. The bonds that connect polypeptide chains and that are responsible for strength and elasticity:

a) peptide          b) side          c) salt          d) disulfide

74. Requires only one end paper to be used in conjunction with other end wrap techniques to cover any remaining hair on the strand:

a) block wrap          b) book end wrap          c) single flat wrap          d) double end

75. _____ is caused by repeated exposure to a chemical substance:

a) Oxidation          b) Lanthionization          c) Neutralization          d) Sensitization

76. A strong alkaline ingredient used in chemical relaxers:

a) alcohol          b) glycerin          c) sodium hydroxide          d) ammonium bilsulfite

# CHEMICAL TEXTURIZING
## STATE BOARD THEORY REVIEW

77. A spiral wrap creates a _____ effect to the hair:

   a) wave
   b) coiling
   c) straight
   d) none of the above

78. The thickness and/or thinness of a liquid is:

   a) no-base
   b) miscible
   c) rebonding
   d) viscosity

79. Sponge rods are made of _____, creating a soft-end result:

   a) pliable foam
   b) hard rubber
   c) flexible plastic
   d) wood dowels

80. _____ rods have an even diameter width throughout the length:

   a) Straight
   b) Curved
   c) Soft
   d) Bender

81. A _____ determines if the required processing time has been reached during a permanent wave:

   a) strand test
   b) test curl
   c) patch test
   d) rod selection

82. A mixture that blends large particles together without dissolving:

   a) suspension
   b) solution
   c) emulsion
   d) miscible solution

83. _____ relaxers are considered to be 'no-lye' relaxers, suitable for soft curl reformation:

   a) Sodium
   b) Keratin
   c) Thioglycolate
   d) Potassium

84. A _____ perm wrap replaces straight partings with zigzag partings:

   a) straight
   b) weave
   c) curved
   d) spiral

85. Applying a solution to stop the permanent wave process and reform the hair into its new curly shape is _____ neutralization:

   a) stabilizer
   b) fixative
   c) thio
   d) sodium

86. The technical term for the study of hair:

   a) dermatology
   b) myology
   c) trichology
   d) physiology

87. Thioglycolic acid is an organic compound of clear liquid with a _____ unpleasant smell:

   a) slight
   b) strong
   c) citrus
   d) neutral

88. Spiraling chains of amino acids joined together by peptide bonds:

   a) polypeptide
   b) salt
   c) hydrogen
   d) end bond

# MY NEED TO KNOW notes:

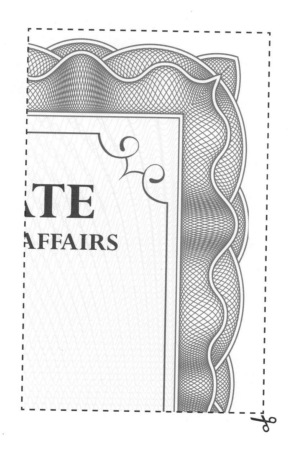

# DESIGN
# PRINCIPLES

# FACE SHAPES | Label each face shape and describe its characteristics.

1. ___Proportion___ is the direct correlation of size, distance, amount and ratio between the individual characteristics when compared with the whole.

2. ___Facial___ ___Proportion___ is the relationship of facial features and shapes to each other.

**OVAL**

is the ideal face shape to achieve.

___Diamond___ Shape

Forehead: ___narrow___

Cheekbones: ___prominent___

Jaw: ___narrow___

___Square___ Shape

Forehead: ___equal in width___

Cheekbones: ___equal___

Jaw: ___equal___

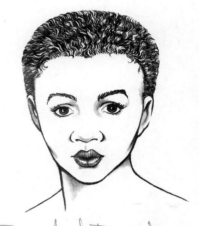

___Inverted Triangle___ Shape

Forehead: ___wide___

Cheekbones: _____

Jaw: ___narrow___

___Round___ Shape

Forehead: ___rounded___

Cheekbones: ___wide___

Jaw: ___rounded___

___Rectangle/oblong___ Shape

Forehead: ___high___

Cheekbones: ___prominent cheekbone___

Jaw: ___angular___

___Triangle/Pear___ Shape

Forehead: ___narrow___

Cheekbones: _____

Jaw: ___wide___

# FACIAL PROPORTION | Draw and label the facial zones.

**Fill in the blanks:**

1. Zone 1 is located between the __hairline__ and the __eyebrow__ __line__.

2. Zone 2 is located between the __eyebrow__ __line__ and the __tip__ of the __nose__.

3. Zone 3 is located between the __tip__ of the __nose__ and the __chin__ __line__.

Zone 1

Zone 2

Zone 3

# PROFILES

In your own words, define profile: _outline of your face from the_
_side_

In your own words, define balance: _____

For each profile, list the characteristics and how to properly balance them. **Pg.497**

### STRAIGHT PROFILE

Forehead: _align_

Nose: _align_

Chin: _align_

Curvature: _straight outward_

Balance by: _ideal_

### CONCAVE PROFILE

Forehead: _protruding_

Nose: _receedes_

Chin: _protruding_

Curvature: _inward_

Balance by: _soft, upward_
_movement_

### CONVEX PROFILE

Forehead: _high hairline_

Nose: _protruding_

Chin: _receedes_

Curvature: _curved_

Balance by: _add fullness moving_
_towards forehead & jawline_
_add volume_

## Label each of the following profiles:

_convex_     _straight_     _concave_

# MY NEED TO KNOW notes:

# PRODUCT CHEMISTRY

Why is it beneficial to understand product chemistry? _____

_____

Describe Volatile Alcohols: evaporate quickly and easily. _____

_____

Describe Volatile Organic Compounds: alcohols that contain carbon and evaporate very quickly.
VOC's found in hairsprays. Carbon forms the "organic" process of a evaporation is the "volatile"

**Mark an 'X' in the box indicating the ingredient classification(s), and list the uses for each product.**

|  | VOLATILE ALCOHOL | VOLATILE ORGANIC COMPOUNDS | USED FOR |
|---|---|---|---|
| Gels | X |  | Curl Definition |
| Hairsprays | X | X | Hold Hair in Place |
| Mousses | X |  | Volume Hold Conditioning |
| Rubbing Alcohol | X |  |  |
| Silicones |  |  | provides high shine silky feel |

# LIQUID TOOLS

*(handwritten annotations at top: "stay in place" / "move it around" / "adds shine")*

| Products | Strength (firm, flexible or finishing) | Use(s) |
|---|---|---|
| Curl Activators | Firm / Flexible | |
| Gels | Firm | |
| Glazes | Flexible / Finish | |
| Glossers | Finishing / Flexible | |
| Hairsprays | Firm / Flexible / Finishing | |
| Mousses / Foams | Flexible | |
| Oil Sheens | Flexible / Finishing | |
| Pastes, Clays and Molding Creams | Flexible / Finishing | |
| Pomades | | |
| Pressing Oils | | |
| Setting Lotions | | |
| Spray Gels | | |
| Styling Straighteners | | |
| Thermal Protectants | | |
| Volumizers | | |
| Waxes | | |
| Working Sprays | | |
| Wrapping Lotions | | |

Your Guest has a natural curl, what products would you use to define and enhance the curl but also hold the style all night?

1. _____    4. _____

2. _____    5. _____

3. _____    6. _____

# BRUSHES

Complete the chart by describing each brush.

| Brush Type | Bristles | Back / Base | Use(s) |
|------------|----------|-------------|--------|
| Cushion    |          |             |        |
| Paddle     |          |             |        |
| Pin        |          |             |        |
| Round      |          |             |        |
| Teasing    |          |             |        |
| Vent       |          |             |        |

## Fill in the blanks.

1. _____ _____ control the amount of curl created by the size of the barrel.

2. _____ _____ brushes are not recommended when blowdrying.

3. _____ bases act as shock absorbers and are gentle on the scalp and hair.

# BLOWDRYER | Label each of the following:

why would you choose to use this?

why would you choose to use this?

why would you choose to use this?

# HAIR PRESSING

**Match the following pressing types with the percentage of curl reduction:**

| Pressing Types | Percentage of Curl Reduction |
|---|---|
| 1. Soft  _C_ | A. 100 |
| 2. Medium  _B_ | B. 60 to 75 |
| 3. Hard  _A_ | C. 50 to 60 |

**Label each of the following:**

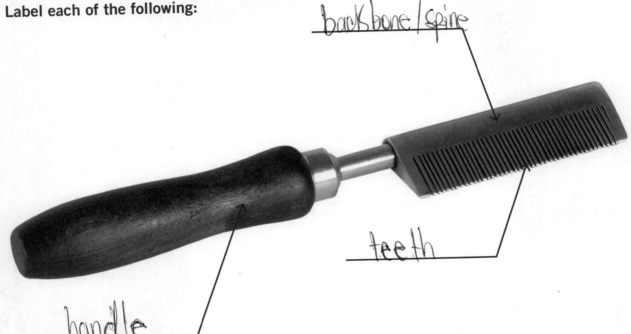

backbone/spine

teeth

handle

**Circle the correct answer:**

1. A method of temporarily straightening highly textured hair by using a heated comb is known as (hair curling or (hair pressing.))

2. Another term for hair pressing is ((thermal hair straightening) or relaxing.)

3. When pressing hair that has a fine texture, you should use (more or (less)) heat and pressure.

4. When pressing hair that has a medium texture, you should use ((standard) or above average) heat and pressure.

5. When pressing hair that has a coarse texture, you should use ((more) or less) heat and pressure.

# THERMAL STYLING TOOLS | Label each of the following:

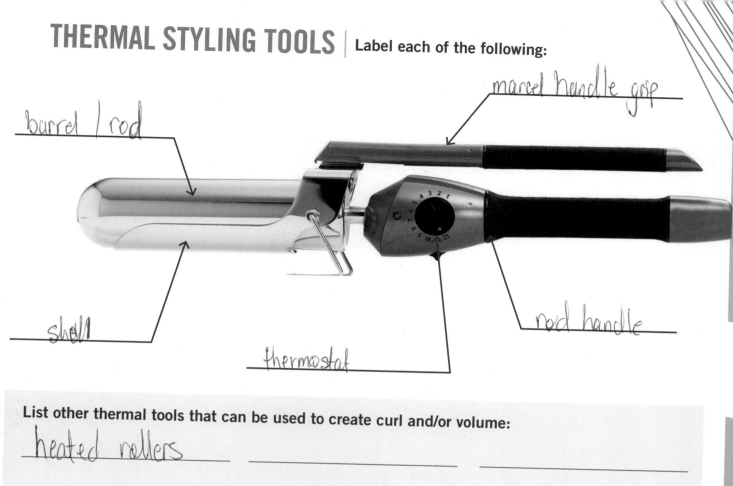

marcel handle grip

barrel / rod

shell

thermostat

rod handle

List other thermal tools that can be used to create curl and/or volume:

heated rollers

pressing plates

on / off

on/off indicator

# TOOL CARE AND MAINTENANCE

**Circle the correct answer.**

**1.** Irons, conventional or electric, can be cleaned and/or sanitized by:

   **a)** wiping with a dry cloth     **b)** wiping with a cloth soaked in alcohol     **(c)** wiping with a damp cloth containing a soap and water solution

**2.** Blowdryers require special attention around the:

   **(a)** air intake area     **b)** power cord     **c)** nozzle

**3.** Electric Hot Rollers should be _____ when wiped down:

   **a)** plugged in     **(b)** unplugged     **c)** turned on

**4.** Hood dryers should be:

   **(a)** wiped down     **b)** vacuumed     **c)** immersed in an EPA-Registered disinfectant

**List 3 important tips to remember when maintaining your tools:**

1. _____

2. _____

3. _____

# DESIGN PRINCIPLES

Label each picture with the correct design principle.

symmetry

rhythm

asymmetry

Emphasis

Repetition

harmony

**Symmetry** is the mirror image from a center point.

**Examples:**

1. _____

2. _____

**Rhythm** is the relationship between movement or motion and the line of a pattern.

**Examples:**

1. waves, finger waves

2. pin curls

**Repetition** is how often the lines, angles, color, and/or shapes repeat.

**Examples:**

1. _____

2. _____

**Harmony** is the esthetic placement of lines and shapes.

**Examples:**

1. _____

2. _____

**Asymmetry** is the non-mirror image from a center point.

**Examples:**

1. _____

2. _____

**Emphasis** is what the eye is drawn to at first glance.

**Examples:**

1. _____

2. _____

# DESIGN ELEMENTS

Design Principles

1. Blowdrying hair in sections while utilizing the comb pick attachment, then flat ironing to complete the straightening process is known as __silk pressing__.

2. __Space__ is the area within or surrounding a hairdesign.

3. __curved__ lines create softness, movement and waves.

4. __form__ is the combination of lines that form the outline of a shape.

## Connect the points to form lines and to create geometric shapes:

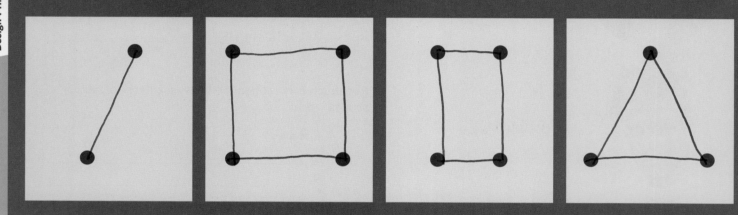

## Draw examples of the following lines:

| VERTICAL | HORIZONTAL | DIAGONAL | CURVED |
|---|---|---|---|

# DESIGN BASICS

1. When using a ___wet styling___ technique, hair is formed into a specific shape and then dried.

2. ___shaping___ , also known as ___molding___ , is combing a section of hair in a circular movement over the surface of the head to form waves or curls.

# CURL CREATION

1. The ___base___
   is the section of hair that is attached to the scalp.

2. The ___stem___
   is the section of hair between the base and the first turn.

3. The ___curl___
   is the end of the hair strand that forms a complete curl or circle.

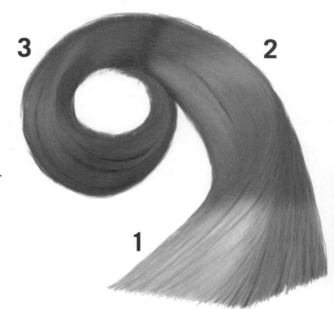

Identify the base used for each curl placement. Then shade in the correct shape, as in the example shown.

1. ___Square___          2. ___rectangle___          3. ___triangle___

# STEM

**In your own words, explain the following:**

Stem: _____

_____

No Stem Curl: _____ on-base _____ , most volume _____
arms held straight out

Half Stem Curl: _____ half-off base , sits on parting off base _____
arms held straight up

Full Stem Curl: _____ off-base , no volume _____
arms held towards you

# CURL PLACEMENT

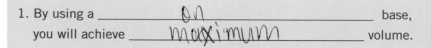

1. By using a _____ on _____ base,
   you will achieve _____ maximum _____ volume.

2. By using a _____ half off _____ base,
   you will achieve _____ medium _____ volume.

3. By using a _____ off _____ base, you will
   achieve freedom of movement and ____ least / minimal ____ volume.

# CURL AND WAVE DESIGN

A. **Fingerwaves**

B. **Barrel Curls**

C. **Volume**

D. **Skipwave**

E. **Indentation**

F. **Ridge Curls**

G. **Pushwave**

1. _F_ flat pincurls following a fingerwave's ridge that produce a strong wave pattern in a finished design

2. _B_ normally created with a rectangle shaped base; used in place of a wet roller application or to support a dry design prior to finishing the style

3. _A_ 'C' shapes placed into the hair in alternating directions using the fingers and a comb

4. _D_ wave pattern that combines fingerwaves and flat pincurls

5. _E_ creates emptiness or flat area(s) in a design

6. _C_ creates lift, fullness or height in a design

7. _G_ another form of fingerwaving that is created by using 2 combs instead of the fingers and is also known as a scrunchwave

# PINCURLS

1. Carved Curls are another name for __sculpture curls__.

2. Stand-Up Pincurls are also known as __Cascade curl__.

3. __ribboning__ is the forcing of hair between your thumb and the back of the comb to create tension.

---

**Label the type of volume achieved: Minimum, Medium, or Maximum.**

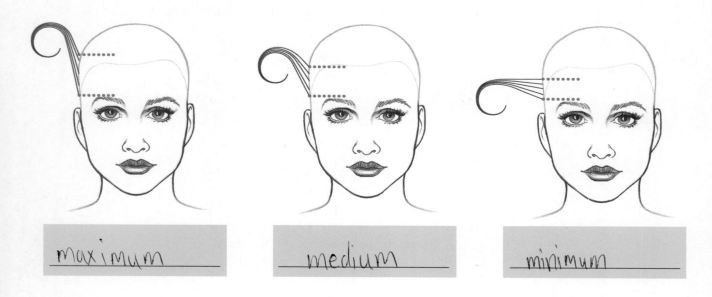

__maximum__          __medium__          __minimum__

---

1. Another term for ruffing is __back-brushing__, and it is performed to provide support and structure to a finished design.

2. __back-combing__ can be applied to the underside of the hair to produce volume, or on the top of the hair to create closeness and movement along with interlocking sections.

3. __polishing__ the design provides the support, texture, and movement to your final design.

# DESIGN FOUNDATIONS

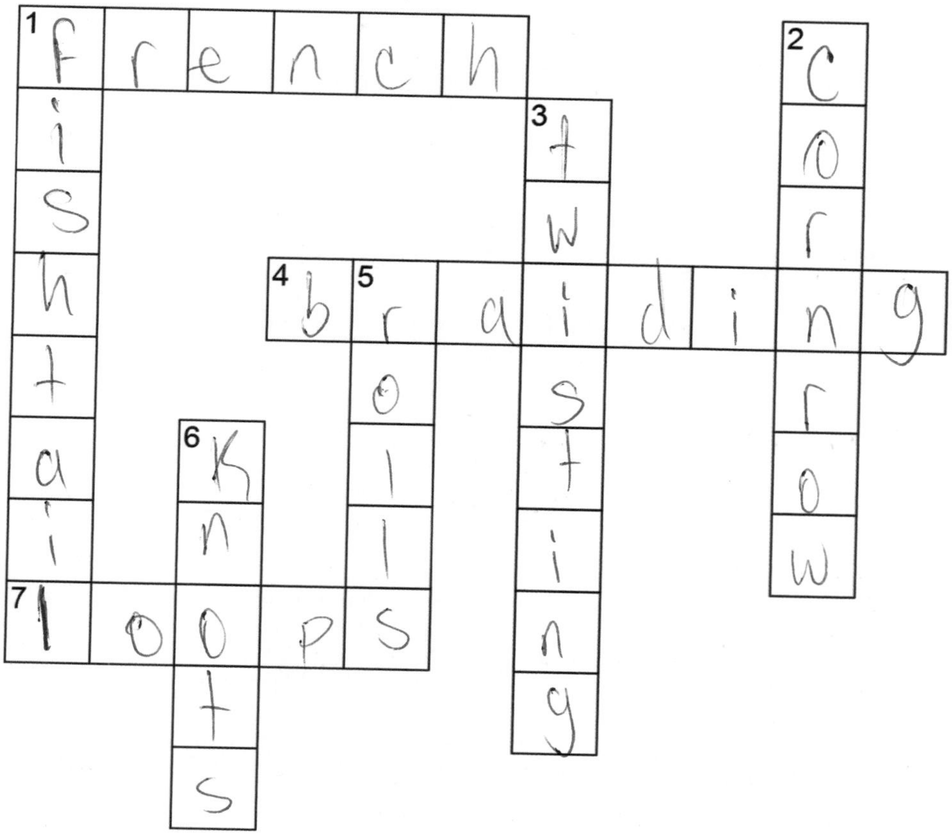
1 french
1 fishtail
2 cornrow
3 twisting
4 braiding
5 rolls
6 knots
7 loops

## DOWN

1. braid created by crossing 2 strands of hair over each other
2. braid created with 3 strands of hair; crossing the outside strands under the center strand
3. winding or intermingling of one or several hair strands
5. consists of hair that is wrapped in a tunnel shape
6. created by tying either one or multiple hair strands together

## ACROSS

1. braid created with 3 strands of hair; crossing the outside strands over the center strand
4. mixing or interweaving of 2 or more strands of hair
7. circular curls that can be formed into any position, shape or size

# NATURAL HAIRSTYLING

Identify and explain each of the following natural texture patterns.

| CURL PATTERN | TEXTURE | SUGGESTED PRODUCTS |
|---|---|---|
| wavy | fine to course | |
| curly | fine to medium | |
| coiled | fine to course | |

What styling options are available for your Guest transitioning from chemically texturized hair to natural hair?

the "Big Chop" or braiding

| Setting Method | Technique | Products to Use |
|---|---|---|
| Free Hand | | |
| Barrel Curls | Curled horizontal | |
| Spiral Curls | Curled virtically | |

| Twisting Method | Technique | Products to Use |
|---|---|---|
| Single Strand | | |
| Two-Strand | | |
| Two-Strand Double | | |
| Flat Two-Strand | | |

| Lock Method | Technique | Products to Use |
|---|---|---|
| Comb | | |
| Palm Roll | | |
| Braid | | |

# HAIR ADDITIONS

```
B O N D I N G L C J R J Q G
T I M P J R W L Y S X K J Y
B S J L D W Z P S G I W A Z
R S O J Q T X G O N F W I U
S N O I T I D D A R I A H C
E T O U P E E Q E B Y R M I
M C X A R G G R A J N C B T
I R E U Y N G L H T Y F N E
P Z W I I G M I O U E R G H
C X S D P Z P L N T M I O T
C U J B R R S Y B S K A Y N
G R W A E B I L Z Q O A N Y
P D V J M S C A A T W Z T S
T S A C Y N D Q H Q B O U G
```

1. _synthetic_ hair additions will melt with the addition of a heat source, such as a curling iron

2. _remy_ a processing technique that tags and aligns the cuticle layers in one direction

3. _human_ hair singes and smells like sulfur when burned

4. _wigs_ artificial hair coverings designed to replace or enhance existing hair

5. _hair piece_ a small wig used to cover small sections of the head

6. _toupe_ a small wig used to cover the top and crown of the head

7. _bonding_ uses a keratin or organic based adhesive and is also known as fusion

8. _hair additions_ natural or synthetic hair attached to the base or scalp area to add length, volume and/or color

# DEVELOPING YOUR DESIGN COMMUNICATION AND SOLUTION SKILLS

What consultation question(s) will you have prepared to ask your Guest for the following:

Formal Style: relaxed/natural, how long is _____

Natural Style: _____

Hair Additions: _____

_____

Your Guest wants an elegant formal design for an event they are attending. What factors should you consider when recommending a style?

_____

_____

The desired style your Guest wants requires a lot of curl and fullness. Would you use rollers, pincurls, a flat iron, and/or a curling iron to create the look? Why?

_____

_____

Your Guest wants a fingerwave style that they have seen on TV, but they have very fine, limp hair. How would you accomplish this look?

_____

_____

## SERVICE RECOMMENDATIONS

What styling recommendations will you discuss with your Guest for the following:

Formal Style:_____

Natural Style:_____

Hair Additions:_____

## MAINTENANCE RECOMMENDATIONS

When discussing a maintenance routine with your Guest, how often will you suggest they rebook for the following services?

Natural Style: _____

Hair Additions: _____

## PRODUCT RECOMMENDATIONS

What product recommendations will you discuss with your Guest and why?

_____

_____

_____

Shampoo:_____

Conditioner:_____

Styling:_____

Finishing:_____

# HEAD DIAGRAM

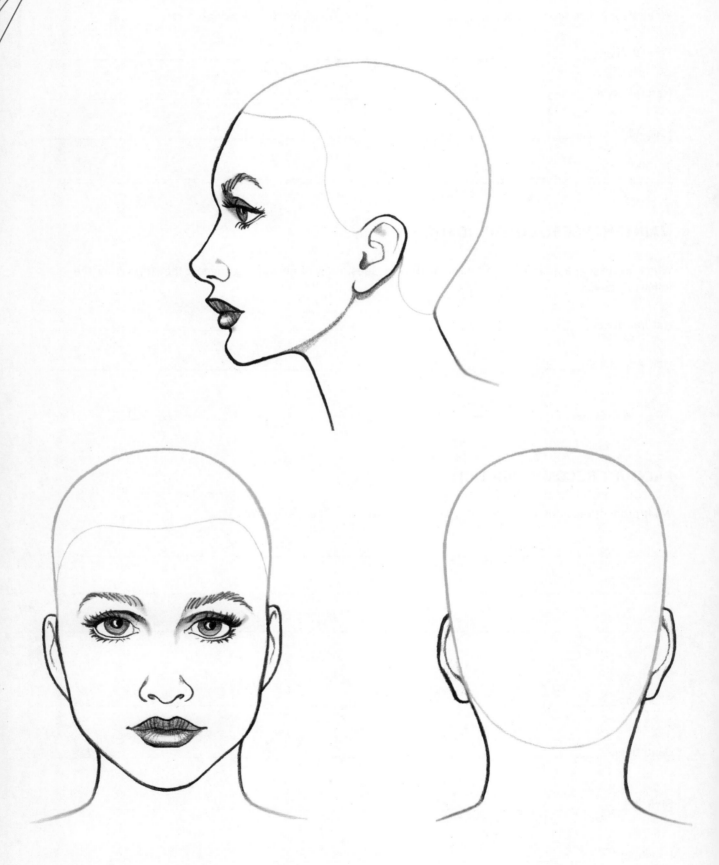

# WORKSHOP
# standards

**MET SKILL**

*Design Principles*

## Safety and Infection Control:

Disinfect work station *(before and after each service)*
Set up work station with required, clean service tools

## Consultation:

Scalp Analysis:  ☐oily  ☐normal  ☐dry  ☐abrasions
Hair Analysis:  ☐density  ☐texture  ☐elasticity  ☐porosity
Drape: neck strip, towel, cape, towel

## Shampoo Bowl Safety:

Maintain control of nozzle at all times, with constant temperature check
Appropriate amount of product is dispensed
Rinse product(s) thoroughly from scalp and hair
Disinfect shampoo bowl and water nozzle

## Fingerwaves:

Proper product saturation and pre-molding of hair
Proper use of comb and finger placement
Blending of ridge and wave – no splits or breaks
Consistent sizing of wave formation(s)

## Pincurls:

Proper sectioning of hair for base required
Curl has accurate stem and circle pattern – avoiding splits
Consistent sizing and placement of pincurl(s)
Secured parallel to stem
Utilization of:  ☐no stem curl  ☐half stem curl  ☐full stem curl

## Braiding:

Section hair according to desired style / design
Strands are of equal size and smoothness
Pick up and proper positioning throughout design completion

## Thermal Styling: *Curling Iron and Flat Iron / Pressing Comb*

Test temperature of thermal appliance using tissue paper
Subsections are parted straight and consistent in relation to size of tool
Utilization and placement of comb between scalp and thermal iron
Secure curls and/or sections of hair when applicable
Hair is free of ridges and/or fishhooks
Allow hair to cool before combing / brushing into style

## Finishing of Service:

Apply appropriate amount and type of fixative(s) to damp / wet hair
Dry hair 80% before using styling brushes
Maintain proper control and temperature of all electrical tools
Complete style as desired
Recommend at-home maintenance product(s)

# SITUATIONAL SCENARIOS

**1.** Jennifer has worn the same hairdesign for the last 4 years; she is ready for a change. During the consultation, you identify that Jennifer has a rectangular shape face with prominent cheekbones, a long, angular chin and a high forehead. What type of hairstyle will best complement Jennifer's face shape?

    **a)** Use soft fringe in the forehead and add fullness around the sides
    **b)** Add softness in the hairdesign and volume in the crown area
    **c)** Add volume in the top and decrease volume along the sides
    **d)** Use curved, soft lines within the design with no fullness, maintaining closeness in the design

**2.** Your appointment, Kim, has just arrived. She is part of a wedding party and requests an updo. You notice that Kim has a beautiful oval face, but has a prominent nose. What styling guidelines should be applied to conceal her nose?

    **a)** Sweep hair straight back away from the face
    **b)** Create volume in forehead and crown while adding softness in the front area
    **c)** The focus of the formal hairdesign should be in line with the nose
    **d)** Focus the hairdesign in the occipital area, with the sides remaining close

**3.** Betty, your regular Guest, has a wet set appointment. You notice that Betty's hair has a build-up of product that appears white and gummy. What type of shampoo should you use?

    **a)** Conditioning shampoo
    **b)** Acid balanced shampoo
    **c)** Clarifying shampoo
    **d)** Dry shampoo

**4.** Joanne, your regular Guest, is going to a party and wants a style from the 1920's or 1930's. She requests a style that when dry is close to the head in a wave formation. What style will need to be created?

    **a)** A wet set
    **b)** A fingerwave set
    **c)** A pincurl set
    **d)** A blowdry and iron set

**5.** Maddie would like to wear her wavy to curly hair straight for her graduation. What tool will you need?

    **a)** Rollers
    **b)** Flat iron
    **c)** Crimping iron
    **d)** Curling iron

**6.** During a consultation, Leslie reveals that she has always had short hair, but secretly wants long hair. She has difficulty letting her fine, thin hair grow long without appearing straggly. You recommend she try extensions that can be added to individual strands to increase the fullness and the length of her hair. What is the best method of attaching the extensions to Leslie's hair?

    **a)** Sew-in method
    **b)** Glue-in method
    **c)** Bonding method
    **d)** Braided method

**7.** Deb is going to begin chemotherapy and would like to purchase a wig of the best quality that will cover her entire head. What type of hair will you need to order for Deb?

    **a)** Human hair wig
    **b)** Synthetic wig
    **c)** Wiglet
    **d)** Fall

**8.** Brenda, a first time Guest, has naturally tightly coiled hair that is prone to frizzing and tangling. She would like to wear her hair natural, but she requires some control. What design technique can you do to assist in defining Brenda's curl pattern?

    **a)** Roller set
    **b)** Wrap
    **c)** Thermal press
    **d)** Twisting technique

**9.** When performing a thermal press on your Guest, Shelly, you notice a lot of steam rising from the pressing comb. Shelly's hair is completely dry. You double check the temperature on a piece of tissue paper to ensure that you have the right amount of heat for her texture. What could be another factor that would cause this?

    **a)** The scalp and hair are overly dry
    **b)** Not using the comb in the correct direction, from scalp to ends
    **c)** Too much product
    **d)** The pressing comb is not hot enough

**10.** During a hair analysis, you determine your Guest, Ty, has thin, fine, layered hair. She would like a hairdesign with maximum fullness. What base placement will you use?

    **a)** On-base
    **b)** Over-directed
    **c)** Under-directed
    **d)** Off-base

**11.** Arriving to work, Jane starts preparing for the day. She begins by cleaning and disinfecting her tools. Jane allows them to become saturated in the disinfectant solution for the appropriate time, then reaches into the jar with tongs, pulls them out and wipes them dry with a towel. What should Jane do next?

    **a)** Neatly arrange all the tools on her station, so throughout the day she will have them readily available
    **b)** Place them in a clean, dry, disinfected container or dry disinfection system
    **c)** Leave them wrapped in the towel in the dispensary
    **d)** Place them in container with water to ensure all the disinfectant is removed from the tools

**13.** As you begin cleaning up at the end of the day, you notice your iron appears to have a build-up of hairspray, dirt and oil. What should you do?

    **a)** Wipe iron with a damp cloth containing a sodium hydroxide solution
    **b)** Wipe iron with a cloth and place in wet sanitizer
    **c)** Wipe iron with a damp cloth containing a soap and water solution; ammonia can be added to this solution, if needed, to assist in removing the build-up
    **d)** Heat iron and use a wet cloth or abrasive pad to scrub the iron clean

# practical PREP

*Each skill will be checked by your Educator and feedback will be provided.*
*Met Skill = 1 point / Not Met Skill = 0 points*

Design Principles

**POINTS**

## Safety and Disinfection:

Disinfects work station *(before and after each service)*

Station set up with required tools

Drapes for set / style service

Performs scalp and hair analysis

Neatly divides and clips hair into 4 quadrants

**Feedback:**

## Braiding: French Braid *(Overhand / Underhand)*:

Sections and smooths strands of equal size

Pick up of and proper cross over / cross under of sections of hair

Continued center positioning of braid in quadrant

**Feedback:**

## Thermal Styling:

**Flat Iron or Pressing Comb:**

Tests temperature of thermal appliance using tissue paper

Subsections parted straight and consistent in size

Prevents burns – utilization and placement of comb between scalp and flat iron

    If using flat iron, continuously slides iron gently down hair section

    If using pressing comb, turns comb and presses hair with back of comb

Hair is free of ridges

**Feedback:**

**Curling Iron:**

Tests temperature of thermal appliance using tissue paper

Subsections are in relation to diameter of curling iron

Prevents burns – utilization and placement of comb between scalp and thermal iron

Demonstrates 2 on-base curls and 2 off-base curls

Partings for subsections are straight and consistent in size

Hair is free of fishhooks

Hair is free of ridges

**Feedback:**

# DESIGN PRINCIPLES
## STATE BOARD THEORY REVIEW

1. Back-brushing is a technique done on the surface of the hair to create a:

   a) compacted,         b) compacted,         c) light,              d) light and
      dense appearance      stacked appearance     dense appearance       airy appearance

2. A way of combing hair that is used to create volume is back-combing, also known as:

   a) cushioning         b) interlocking        c) lacing, matting     d) all the above
                                                    and ratting

3. Barrel curls are a type of pincurl, used in place of a wet roller application that have a _____ shaped base:

   a) rectangle          b) round               c) oval                d) triangle

4. Non-mirror image with unequal lengths:

   a) symmetry           b) asymmetry           c) balance             d) harmony

5. _____ is the section of hair that is attached to the scalp:

   a) Circle             b) Stem                c) Base                d) Curl

6. A method of attaching artificial hair to natural hair by using an adhesive:

   a) bonding            b) sewing              c) braiding            d) weaving

7. _____ have the stem and base raised, while the ends turn under:

   a) Cascade curls      b) Sculpture curls     c) Ridge curls         d) Skip curls

8. The visual comparison of weight to offset or equalize proportion:

   a) design             b) texture             c) movement            d) balance

9. Carved curls are also known as:

   a) cascade curls      b) sculpture curls     c) ridge curls         d) skip curls

10. Because of their receding chin, protruding nose, and high hairline, people with this facial profile look good
    with full bangs and added volume at or below the chin.

   a) convex profile     b) concave profile     c) straight profile    d) hollow profile

11. _____ is the end of the hair strand that forms a complete circle:

a) Curl     b) Stem     c) Base     d) Beginning

12. A line that creates softness and/or waves:

a) straight     b) diagonal     c) curved     d) zigzag

13. Curl is also known as:

a) base     b) stem     c) circle     d) shaping

14. An area in a design that is the highlight or of the most importance:

a) harmony     b) repetition     c) balance     d) emphasis

15. Concave profile has a protruding chin and forehead which moves:

a) outward     b) inward     c) flat     d) square

16. The seven face shapes are characterized by a person's:

a) bone structure and hairline     b) eyes, chin and cheeks     c) chin, nose and mouth     d) cheeks, jaw and eyes

17. A wet setting technique using 'C' shapes that are placed into the hair in alternating directions:

a) fingerwaving     b) circle     c) curl     d) none of the above

18. The relationship of facial features and shape to each other.

a) facial emphasis     b) facial rhythm     c) facial proportion     d) facial contrast

19. Hair pressing:

a) permanently waves the hair     b) temporarily curls straight hair     c) temporarily straightens curly hair     d) gives wide waves to curly hair

20. Form is a combination of lines that outline a:

a) texture     b) line     c) shape     d) face

# DESIGN PRINCIPLES
## STATE BOARD THEORY REVIEW

21. Hair additions are made of either:

   a) natural hair          b) synthetic hair          c) both a and b          d) none of the above

22. Hairpieces primarily cover what area(s) of the head:

   a) sides          b) nape          c) top / crown          d) none of the above

23. In wet setting a pincurl, when you use a full stem base, it will produce:

   a) the most          b) the least          c) an equal          d) an over-directed curl
      amount of curl          amount of curl          amount of curl

24. _____ placement sits off its base; produces minimal volume and maximum movement:

   a) On-base          b) Half off-base          c) Off-base          d) Indentation

25. The removal of the curl pattern, using the pressing comb twice on each side of the hair strand:

   a) soft press          b) hard press          c) single press          d) both b and c

26. To create a style with medium movement and curl, what type of curl placement is used:

   a) full-stem          b) no stem          c) on-base          d) half stem

27. An attractive arrangement that incorporates all of the elements of design has:

   a) contrast          b) repetition          c) harmony          d) emphasis

28. A form of natural hairstyling:

   a) locks          b) fishtail braid          c) overlap braid          d) loops

29. Medium press is a hair straightening technique that removes:

   a) 30 to 45% of curl     b) 50 to 100% of curl     c) 60 to 75% of curl     d) 75 to 100% of curl

30. Indentation can be defined as all of the following words except:

   a) emptiness          b) flat area          c) volume          d) hollow

31. Molding is also known as:

   a) ridge          b) outlining          c) shaping          d) perimeter

# DESIGN PRINCIPLES
## STATE BOARD THEORY REVIEW

32. To create a style with maximum volume, use a curl:

a) on-base     b) half off-base     c) off-base     d) under-directed

33. Continued rotation of a round brush on the ends of hair, for a smoother, neat, and frizz-free finish:

a) base placement     b) polishing     c) barrel curling     d) waving

34. Base placement that achieves the greatest amount of volume and sits within its parts:

a) on-base     b) half off-base     c) off-base     d) under-directed

35. The profile of the face from one side is also known as:

a) outline     b) contour     c) both a and b     d) neither a nor b

36. Scrunchwaves are also known as:

a) pushwaves     b) skipwaves     c) ridgewaves     d) pencilwaves

37. When you desire a style with the least amount of movement, what type of curl do you use:

a) full stem curl     b) half stem curl     c) no stem curl     d) slow speed curl

38. The direct correlation of size, distance, amount and ratio between the individual charasteristics when compared to the whole:

a) repetition     b) harmony     c) balance     d) proportion

39. A fingerwave pattern uses what design principle:

a) rhythm     b) contrast     c) proportion     d) all of the above

40. Ribboning involves a great deal of:

a) tension     b) balance     c) lift     d) volume

41. The molded section of a fingerwave is known as the:

a) ridge     b) shaping     c) wave     d) hollow

42. Ridge curls follow and support a fingerwave's:

a) shell     b) ridge     c) ends     d) shape

# DESIGN PRINCIPLES
## STATE BOARD THEORY REVIEW

43. Skipwaves are wave patterns using _____ pincurls:

a) volume     b) barrel     c) flat     d) round

44. A _____ uses two combs to create a three-dimensional form:

a) pushwave     b) scrunchwave     c) skipwave     d) both a and b

45. To create texture and/or movement for a style, use a _____ curl:

a) stem     b) indentation     c) sculpture     d) volume

46. Blowdrying and flat ironing hair into a straight form:

a) silk press     b) soft press     c) hard press     d) double press

47. A wig can replace your Guest's hair, or it can be a:

a) fashion accessory     b) fingerwave     c) hat     d) silk press

48. A design element that allows for open areas in a design:

a) texture     b) color     c) form     d) space

49. To straighten hair with a soft press technique, use a thermal pressing comb:

a) once on the top side of the hair shaft     b) once on each side of the hair shaft     c) once on the top side and twice on the bottom side of the hair shaft     d) twice on each side of the hair shaft

50. A profile with the nose, forehead and chin aligned, creating a slight outward curvature:

a) concave profile     b) convex profile     c) straight profile     d) none of the above

51. Stand-up pincurls are also known as:

a) cascade pincurls     b) flat pincurls     c) ridge pincurls     d) sculpture pincurls

52. Volatile organic compounds contain:

a) oxygen     b) hydrogen     c) sulfur     d) carbon

53. _____ is the section of hair located between the base and the curl:

a) Base          b) Stem          c) Shaping          d) Circle

54. Thermal hair straightening is also known as:

a) thermal blowdrying     b) thermal curling     c) hair pressing     d) keratin straightening

55. Harmony results from balanced proportion known as:

a) symmetry          b) asymmetry          c) counterbalance          d) off balance

56. Volatile alcohols evaporate:

a) quickly but irregularly     b) quickly and easily     c) slowly and irregularly     d) slowly but regularly

57. Wet styling is setting the hair into a specific:

a) shape          b) hollowness          c) size          d) height

58. Volume base creates all of the following except:

a) lift          b) hollowness          c) fullness          d) height

59. A curl or roller that sits totally off its base is known as:

a) off-base          b) on-base          c) half off-base          d) none of the above

60. When the chin and forehead align creating an inward curvature of the face, we refer to this as a _____ profile:

a) straight          b) convex          c) concave          d) perfect

**My Need to Know Notes:**

_____

_____

_____

_____

_____

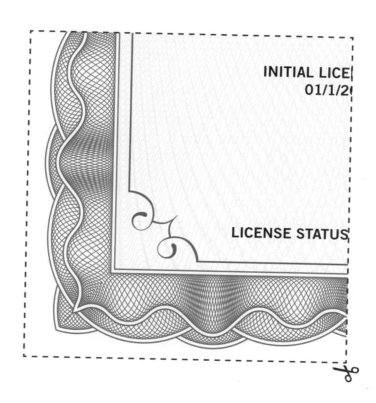

INITIAL LICE
01/1/2(

LICENSE STATUS

# SKIN CARE

# SAFETY AND DISINFECTION | CROSSWORD PUZZLE

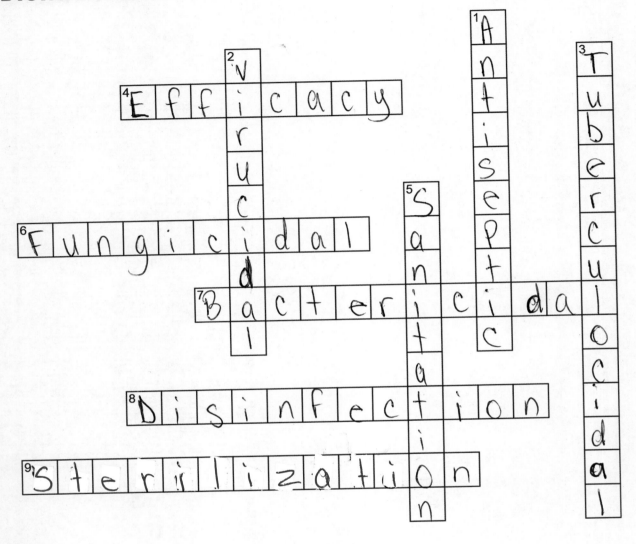

## ACROSS

**4.** the ability to produce favorable results

**6.** capable of destroying fungi

**7.** capable of destroying bacteria

**8.** destroying microorganisms on nonporous surfaces; the second level of decontamination

**9.** chemical process that completely destroys all microbial life; the highest level of decontamination

## DOWN

**1.** can be applied to the skin to clean a wound or help remove bacteria

**2.** capable of destroying viruses

**3.** capable of destroying tuberculosis

**5.** physical or chemical process of removing surface pathogens and dirt

Skin Care

# BACTERIOLOGY

1. _Bacteria_ are one-celled microorganisms that can only be seen through a microscope.
2. _Non-Pathogenic_ are microorganisms that do not cause harm or disease.
3. _Pathogenic_ are microorganisms that cause harm or disease.
4. _bloodborne Pathogens_ are infectious pathogenic microorganisms that are present in human blood or bodily fluids.
5. _staphylococci_ are bacterial cells that form in clusters, form pus and produce boils.
6. _Diplococci_ are bacterial cells that grow in pairs, are spherical-shaped and cause pneumonia.
7. _streptococci_ are pus-forming bacterial cells that form in long chains.
8. _Bacilli_ are long rod-shaped bacteria that cause tetanus (lockjaw)
9. _Spirilla_ are spiral-shaped, curved bacteria that cause syphilis and lyme disease.

---

**In your own words, give the definitions of the following:**

pg. 688

| | DEFINITION |
|---|---|
| Hepatitis | |
| Herpes Simplex | |
| HIV | |
| AIDS | |
| MRSA | |

# ANATOMY

Locate the following words in your textbook. List the page number on which you find the term and provide its definition.

| | PAGE NUMBER | DEFINITION |
|---|---|---|
| Cell | 692 | basic units of all living matter. |
| Mitosis | 693 | Process in which human tissue cells reproduce, by dividing in half, creating 2 daughter cells |
| Organs | 694 | separate body structures, composed of multiple tissues that each individually, perform specific functions |
| Protoplasm | 692 | jelly-like, granular material that contains the living contents of a cell |
| Tissues | 693 | Groups of similar cells that perform a specific function |

Label: Cytoplasm; Cell Membrane; Nucleus.

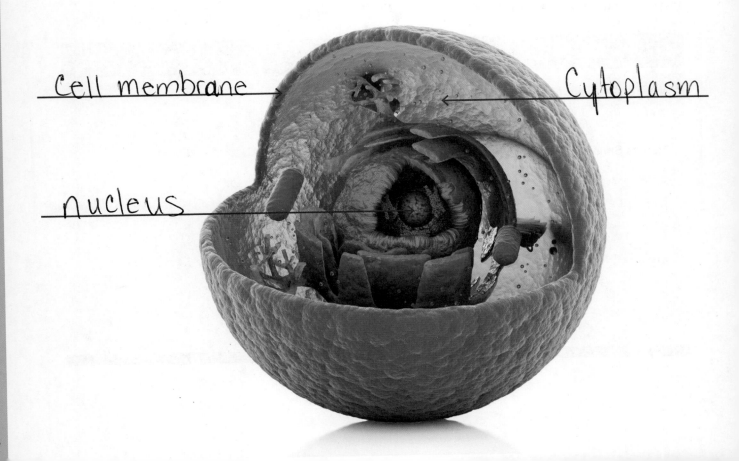

Cell membrane → 

← Cytoplasm

nucleus

# MY NEED TO KNOW notes:

# 11 BODY SYSTEMS | Complete the chart below.

| BODY SYSTEM | ORGANS | FUNCTION |
|---|---|---|
| 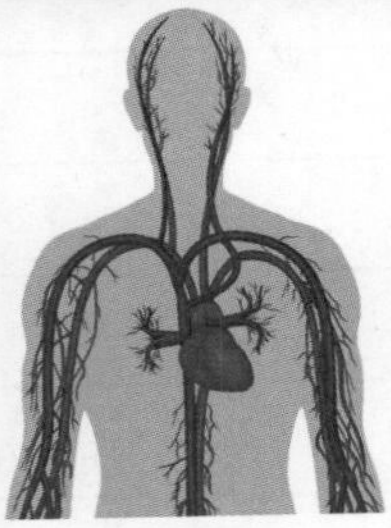 circulatory | Heart, blood, blood vessels | moving blood & lymph throughout the body |
| 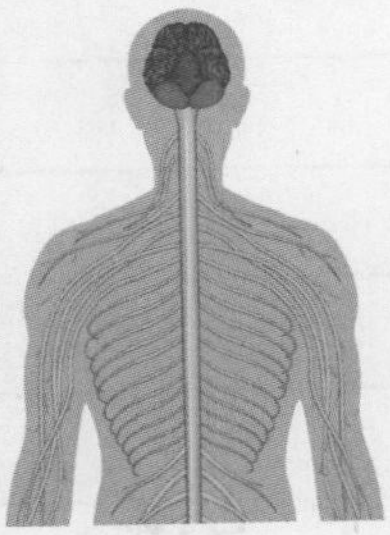 Nervous | brain, spinal cord, nerves | regulates and controls all of the body's activities |
| 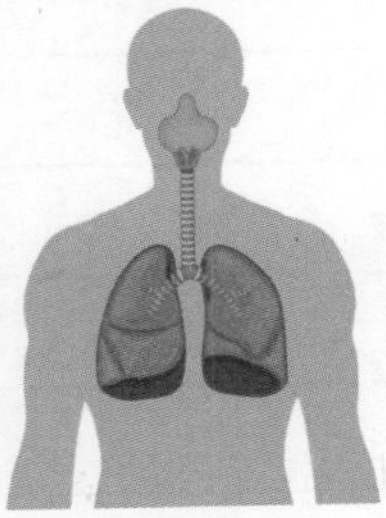 Respiratory | two sac-like organs lungs | Processes air |
| 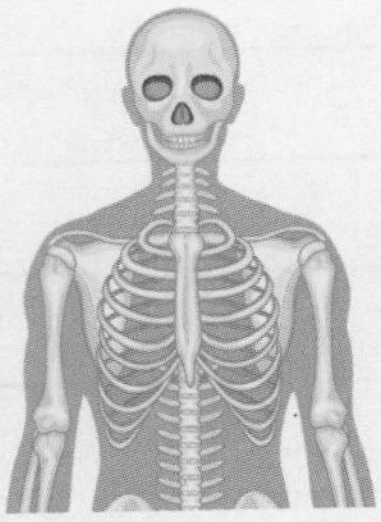 Skeletal | 206 bones | physical foundation of the body, |
| 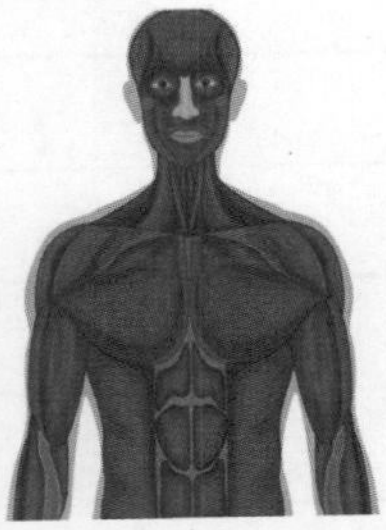 Muscular | Muscles | contracts + moves various parts of the body, supports the skeletal system |
| 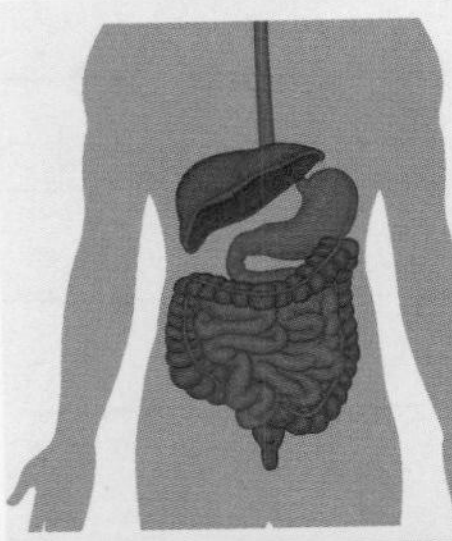 Digestive | stomach intestines mouth several glands | Breaks food down into nutrients |

| | BODY SYSTEM | ORGANS | FUNCTION |
|---|---|---|---|
| | Endocrine | thyroid gland, pituitary gland<br>Ductless glands | • regulate hormone production |
| | Excretory | Kidneys<br>liver<br>skin<br>large intestine<br>lungs | Eliminates waste from the body |
| | Integumentary | Skin and its layers | Serves as protective covering |
| | Lymphatic / Immune | lymph nodes<br>lymph capillaries<br>blood vessels | develop immunities to protect the body from disease. |
| | Reproductive | Reproductive organs | reproduction |

Which body system is responsible for the Pituitary and Thyroid Glands? __Endocrine__

What is the Pituitary Gland responsible for? controls most every physiological process throughout the human body; growth, metabolism, sexual organ functions, contractions during birth, breast milk production + blood pressure.

What is the Thyroid Gland responsible for? controls how quickly the body burns energy, makes proteins, and how sensitive the body should be to other hormones

# BONES OF THE FACE

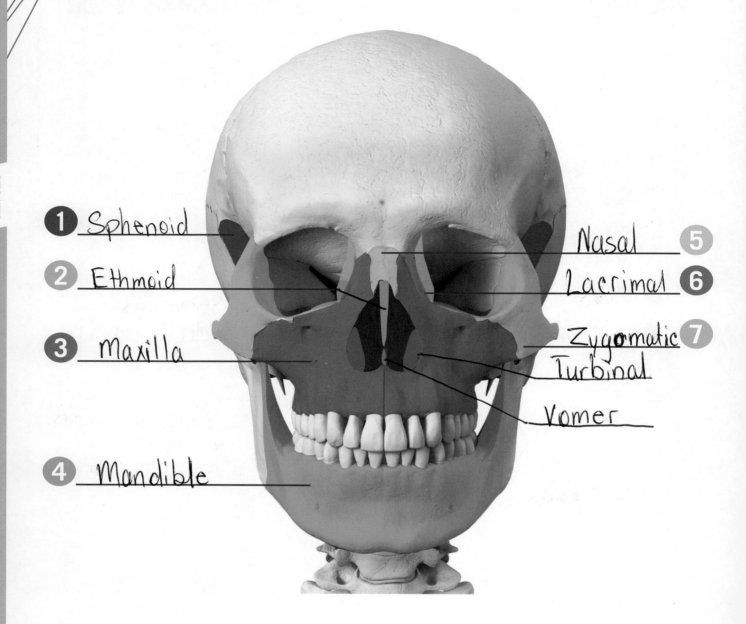

1 Sphenoid
2 Ethmoid
3 Maxilla
4 Mandible

Nasal 5
Lacrimal 6
Zygomatic 7
Turbinal
Vomer

1. a wedge-shaped bone that joins all the bones of the cranium

2. a spongy bone between both eye sockets that forms part of the nasal cavity

3. 2 bones that form the upper jaw

4. the largest and strongest facial bone; forms the lower jaw

5. 2 bones that form the bridge of the nose

6. the small, thin bones located at the front inner wall of the eye socket

7. 2 bones, one on each side of the face, that form the cheekbones

# BONES OF THE NECK AND CHEST

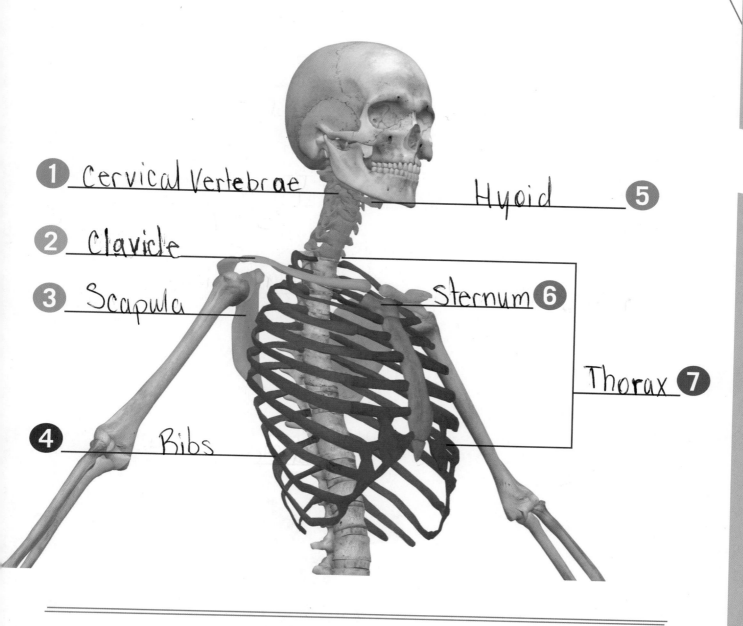

1 Cervical Vertebrae

2 Clavicle

3 Scapula

4 Ribs

Hyoid 5

Sternum 6

Thorax 7

1. 7 bones that make up the portion of the spinal column in the neck
2. a long bone located at the upper part of the chest connecting the sternum and the scapula; also known as the collarbone
3. 2 large, flat bones that form the back part of the shoulder blades
4. 12 pairs of bones that are located on the lower part of the thorax
5. a horseshoe-shaped bone located in the throat; also known as the 'Adam's Apple'
6. a long, flat bone that connects and supports the ribs; also known as the breastbone
7. located between the neck and abdomen; also known as the chest

# MUSCLES | CROSSWORD PUZZLE

## ACROSS

**5.** portion of the muscle that is joined to the bone to aid in movement

**6.** voluntary muscles that are knowingly controlled

**7.** muscle that controls the heart

## DOWN

**1.** involuntary muscles that are smooth

**2.** the scientific study of the structure, functions and diseases of the muscles

**3.** the portion of the muscle attached to the non-movable part of the bone

**4.** the middle part of the muscle

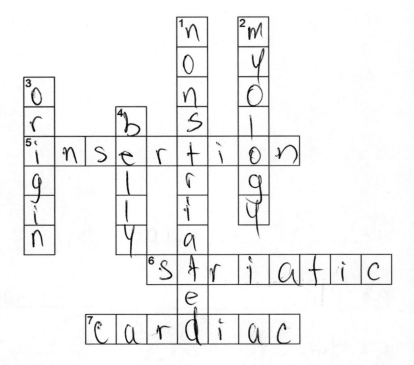

The crossword grid filled in:
- 1 down: n o n s t r i a t e d
- 2 down: m y o l o g y
- 3 down: o r i g i n
- 4 down: b e l l y
- 5 across: i n s e r t i o n
- 6 across: s t r i a t e d
- 7 across: c a r d i a c

# MUSCLES OF THE EAR

T

**1** auriculairs Posterior

**2** Auricularis Superior

**3** Auricularis Anterior

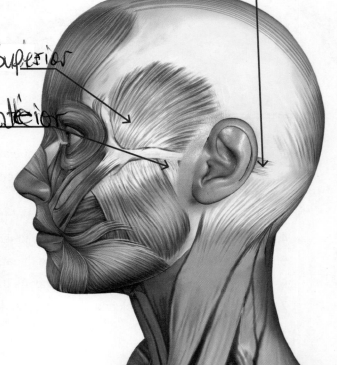

**1.** located behind the ear and can move the ear backward

**2.** located at the top of the ear and can move the ear upward

**3.** located in front of the ear and can move the ear forward

# MUSCLES OF THE FACE

1. surrounds the entire eye socket; allows the eye to open and close

2. elevates the upper lip and flares the nostrils

3. located at the bridge of the nose between the eyebrows; pulls the eyebrows down, causing them to wrinkle

4. located between the eyebrows; pulls the eyebrows downward and wrinkles vertically

5. lies above the orbicularis oris; helps lift the upper lips to produce a snarl; also known as the muscle caninus

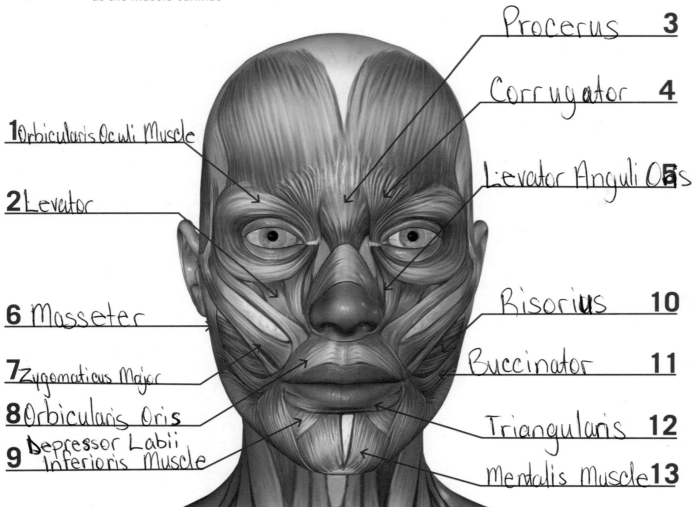

Procerus **3**

Corrugator **4**

1 Orbicularis Oculi Muscle

Levator Anguli Oris **5**

2 Levator

6 Masseter

Risorius **10**

Buccinator **11**

7 Zygomaticus Major

8 Orbicularis Oris

Triangularis **12**

9 Depressor Labii Inferioris Muscle

Mentalis Muscle **13**

6. located in the cheek; aids in closing the jaw during chewing

7. located at the outside corner of the mouth; pulls the mouth up and back to create a smile

8. flat; encompassing the entire mouth; used in blowing, puckering or whistling

9. located below the lower lip; lowers the lip down and/or to the side to express sarcasm

10. located at the corner of the mouth; pulls the mouth up and out, creating a grin

11. thin, flat muscle located between the upper and lower jaw; compresses the cheek for blowing and chewing

12. long muscle stretching from the corner of the mouth to the chin; pulls the mouth down, expressing sadness

13. located at the tip of the chin; elevates the lower lip and wrinkles the chin

# CIRCULATORY AND
# LYMPHATIC SYSTEMS pg. 703-707

1. _Blood_ a nourishing fluid that circulates throughout the body, supplying oxygen and nutrients to cells

2. _Hemoglobin_ an iron supporting protein that is contained within red blood cells

3. _Platelets_ also known as thrombocytes, are tiny color-free particles in the blood responsible for clotting or coagulation

4. _Atriums_ the thin-walled chambers on the top half of the heart

5. _Ventricles_ the thick-walled chambers on the bottom half of the heart

6. _Valves_ permit the blood to travel in only one direction

7. _Lymph_ a clear, slightly yellow fluid that is filtered by the lymph nodes

8. _Common_ _Carotid_ _Arteries_ the main source of blood supply to the head, face and neck

9. _Veins_ thin-walled, tube-like vessels that carry impure blood back to the heart

10. _Arteries_ thick-walled, tube-like vessels that carry oxygen-rich blood away from the heart

# ARTERIES
# OF THE FACE

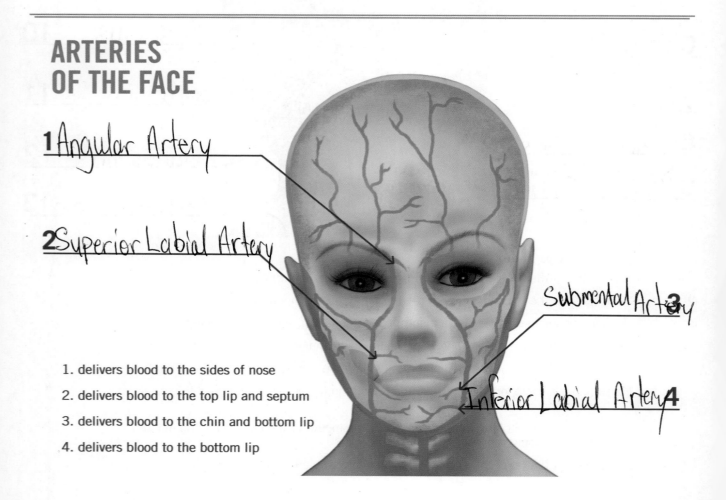

1 Angular Artery

2 Superior Labial Artery

Submental Artery 3

Inferior Labial Artery 4

1. delivers blood to the sides of nose
2. delivers blood to the top lip and septum
3. delivers blood to the chin and bottom lip
4. delivers blood to the bottom lip

# ARTERIES OF THE FACE AND NECK

Pg. 707

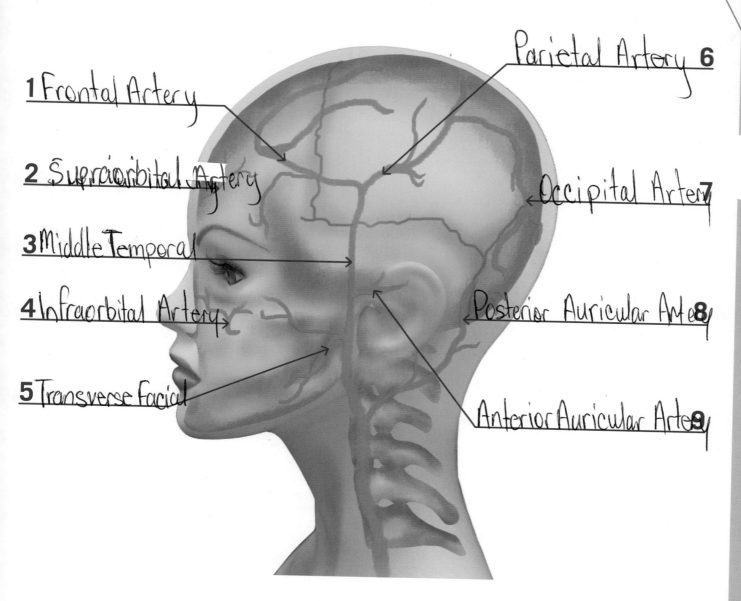

**1** Frontal Artery

**2** Supraorbital Artery

**3** Middle Temporal

**4** Infraorbital Artery

**5** Transverse Facial

**6** Parietal Artery

**7** Occipital Artery

**8** Posterior Auricular Artery

**9** Anterior Auricular Artery

1. delivers blood to the upper eyelids and forehead as a branch of the External Carotid Artery

2. delivers blood to the upper eyelids and forehead

3. delivers blood to the temples

4. delivers blood to the eye muscles

5. delivers blood to the cheek muscles and skin

6. delivers blood to the sides and crown of head

7. delivers blood to the scalp and muscles of the crown and back of head

8. delivers blood to the skin and scalp area

9. delivers blood to the front area of the ears

A. **Motor Nerve**

B. **Fifth Cranial Nerve**

C. **Eleventh Cranial Nerve**

D. **Seventh Cranial Nerve**

E. **Greater Occipital Nerve**

F. **Sensory Nerve**

G. **Autonomic Nervous System**

H. **Peripheral Nervous System**

I. **Mental Nerve**

1. **C.** a motor nerve that controls the motion of the neck and shoulder muscles; also known as the accessory nerve

2. **A.** nerve that carries messages to the brain and/or spinal cord to produce movement

3. **B.** largest of the cranial nerves; also known as the Trifacial or Trigeminal Nerve

4. **D.** the Facial Nerve

5. **G.** regulates involuntary body functions

6. **H.** consists of a group of nerves and nerve cells that connect every part of the body

7. **F.** nerve that carries messages to the brain and/or spinal cord to recognize touch

8. **I.** expands into the skin of the bottom lip and chin area

9. **E.** involves the upper part of the occipitalis muscle

# SKIN BASICS
List the 6 functions of the skin and the purpose of each.

Pg. 712

**FUNCTION** | **PURPOSE**

1. **Protection** — guarding against the skin's enemies

2. **Heat Regulation** — maintaining body temp of 98.6°, through the circulation of blood and excretion of perspiration

3. **Absorption** — allows products to penetrate the skin, helps to retain the stretch/elasticity

4. **Secretion** — when sebum, oily substance, provides moisture and maintain the skins elasticity

5. **Excretion** — when sweat glands disperse perspiration. maintains healthy temp. by cooling the body

6. **Sensation** — touch, heat, cold, pressure + pain receptors that stimulate the nerve endings. The receptors near the hair follicles within the dermis and send messages to the brain to react to sensation

# LAYERS OF THE SKIN  pg. 713

Stratum Corneum

Stratum Lucidum

Stratum Granulosum

Stratum Spinosm

Stratum Germinativum

Sebaceous Gland

Arrector Pili

- Arrector Pili
- Sebaceous Gland
- Stratum Corneum
- Stratum Germinativum
- Stratum Granulosum
- Stratum Lucidum
- Stratum Spinosum

Pg. 713

Duct Gland

Epidermis (The Basal Layer)

Dermis (Inner layer)

Sudoriferous (Sweat Gland)

Skin Care

- Dermis
- Duct Gland

- Epidermis

- Sudoriferous Gland

Name the 2 layers of the Dermis:

papillary                    reticular

# PIGMENTATIONS OF SKIN pg. 719

What role do Melanocytes play in skin pigmentation? Cell producing Melanin which gives color. Contains the pigment granules called melanosomes

**In your own words describe Hypopigmentation:** light patches, absence of pigment, white patches, devoid of pigment / melanin.

| Examples | Characteristics |
|---|---|
| Leukoderma | light patches |
| Albinism | total/partial lack of melanin / skin & hair are white - eyes are pink/red |
| Vitiligo | smooth, irregularly shaped white patches |

**In your own words describe Hyperpigmentation:** dark patches / spots, darker than normal,

| Examples | Characteristics |
|---|---|
| chloasma (liver spots/moth patches) | non-elevated, light-dark scattered spots |
| Lentigines (freckles) | small, flat, colored spots (various colors, shapes, siz |
| Nevus (birthmark) | raised/non-raised, small/large, mark/stain on skin, brown/reddish-purple shades |

# SKIN GROWTHS

**In your own words describe Hypertrophy:** excessive/abnormal growth of skin, generally benign

| Examples | Characteristics |
|---|---|
| Keratoma (callus) (Tyloma) | thick/hard skin caused by friction |
| skin tag | small, soft, pigmented outgrowth of the epidermal |
| Verruca (wart) | hard, rough, red/flesh colored bump. On hands/feet |
| mole | light/dark brown, small flat/raised spot |

# SKIN CANCER

**What is Melanoma?** tumor with dark pigment + is typically associated with skin cancer.

| | CHARACTERISTICS | LAYER OF SKIN |
|---|---|---|
| **Basal Cell Carcinoma** | most common, mildest/non-melanoma small red bump with a surface appearance of blood vessels / a 'pearly' nodule with a rough texture. | stratum germinativum |
| **Squamous Cell Carcinoma** | red, scaly patches / open sores that may bleed/crust. more serious than Basal Cell Carcinoma | epidermis |
| **Malignant Melanoma** | most dangerous form, dark brown/black spots or lesions with uneven shape and/or texture. | stratum germinativum papillary layers |

# CANCER A,B,C,D,E's | What does each letter stand for?

| | STANDS FOR: | DESCRIPTION: |
|---|---|---|
| A | Asymmetry | Both halves look the same |
| B | Border | Smooth, not jagged or irregular |
| C | Color | Varied shades of brown, black, red, blue or white |
| D | Diameter | Larger or smaller than .24 inches |
| E | Evolving | Shape or size changing, itching, bleeding |

# DISORDERS OF THE SKIN

**Explain the following:**

Acute: Short duration, but can be severe and painful

Chronic: Long-lasting or recurring

Systemic Disease: due to over-functioning / under-functioning internal glands / organs.

| DISORDERS | CHARACTERISTICS | SERVICE (YES / NO) |
|---|---|---|
| **SEBACEOUS GLANDS** | | |
| Comedone – Blackhead / open | hair follicles containing masses of hardened sebum and keratin. Follicle is open | yes |
| Comedone – Whitehead / closed remain closed | hair follicles, keeping the sebum from being exposed. | yes |
| Milia | small, white keratin-filled bumps or cysts. Enclosed within the epidermis. Found around eyes, cheeks and forehead. | yes |
| Acne | pus filled pimples with red and swollen appearance. chronic inflammation of sebaceous gland | yes |
| Rosacea | mostly on nose and cheeks, over-dilation of the tiny blood vessels. prickly heat / heat rash | yes |
| **SUDORIFEROUS GLANDS** | | |
| Bromhidrosis | foul smelling sweat as a result of its bacterial breakdown | ~~yes / no~~ yes |
| Anhidrosis | lack of perspiration due to an underactive sudoriferous gland. | yes |
| Hyperhidrosis | over-abundance of perspiration or an unusual increase of sweating due to overactive sudoriferous glands | yes |
| Miliaria Rubra | prickly heat / heat rash. Rash of tiny, red, raised spots, with burning and itching. | yes |
| **OTHER INFLAMMATORY DISORDERS** | | |
| Conjunctivitis / Pinkeye | pink / red eye, highly contagious | NO |
| Dermatitis | redness, swelling, itching, blistering inflammation of the skin ⟩ non | ~~No~~ yes |
| Dermatitis Venenata (contact Dermatitis) | redness, swelling, itching, blistering allergic reaction | ~~no~~ yes |
| Eczema | painful, itchy, non-contagious skin inflammation. | yes ~~no~~ |
| Impetigo | contagious, small sore, then group of blisters filled with a yellow-brown liquid | NO |

222

# DISORDERS OF THE SKIN

What is a lesion: <u>wound or mark of the skin. Can be considered a disease or disorder</u>

| LESIONS | CHARACTERISTICS | SERVICE (YES / NO) |
|---|---|---|
| PRIMARY pg. 726 | different skin color and are raised above the skin | ~~No~~ / yes |
| Macule | flat, small colored spots, vary in color, shape and size freckles or birthmarks | yes |
| Papule | small, red elevated protrusion of the skin, usually containing no pus | ~~No~~ yes |
| Vesicle | small elevated blister or sac filled with a clear fluid. within/directly below the epidermis (poison ivy/cold sores) | No |
| Bulla | large blister containing clear, watery fluid | ~~No~~ yes |
| Pustule | inflamed, elevated pimple containing pus. Red area swollen due to underlying pus. | ~~No~~ yes |
| Wheal / Urticaria | itchy, swollen lesion, shortly after insect bite or allergic reaction. | ~~No~~ yes |
| Tumor | abnormal solid mass or lump varying in size, shape and color | No |
| SECONDARY pg. 727 | structural change to the skin surface | |
| Scale | shedding dead skin cells | ~~No~~ yes |
| Crust (scab) | dried and hardened accumulation of blood, sebum or pus; scab | No |
| Excoriation | existing scratched sore. scraping or scratching of the epidermal layer | No |
| Fissure | opening or crack in skin. May penetrate down into the dermal layer. | ~~No~~ yes |
| Scar | raised, discolored marks that appear when an injury is healing | yes |
| Ulcer | slow-healing, open lesion, on the surface of the skin or mucus membrane. | No |

Skin Care

223

# ELECTROTHERAPY | FILL IN THE BLANKS pg.732

T 1. Tesla High Frequency Current , also known as Violet Ray , produces heat and provides stimulation.

2. Modalities, are the currents used during electrical facial and scalp treatments.

3. Microcurrents are the low level electrical currents that are similar to the electrical currents produced by the human body.

T 4. Low Galvanic Current is a constant and direct current, set to a safe low voltage level, used to create chemical changes when combined with solutions containing acids and salts.

# ELECTROTHERAPY | MATCHING

A. Iontophoresis

B. Polarity

C. Cathode

D. Anode

1. B property of having two opposites; a positive and negative pole of an electric current

2. A the process of forcing a water-based soluble solution into the skin using a galvanic current

3. D the positive electrode

4. C the negative electrode

Iontophoresis

Cataphoresis - uses the positive pole to produce temporary effects on the area being treated.

Anaphoresis - uses the negative pole to produce temporary effects on the area being treated

Desincrustation - use of alkaline solution along with the electric current, will liquefy (melt) the sebum/oily deposits and dirt to aid in removal/extraction.

# ELECTRICITY | WORD SEARCH

1. _Kilowatt_ 1,000 watts of electrical power used within one second

2. _Ampere (Amp)_ the unit for measuring the strength of an electric current

3. _milliampere_ less than 1/1000 of an ampere

4. _Volt_ the unit for measuring the force or pressure of an electric current

5. _Ohm_ the unit for measuring the resistance of an electric current

6. _Watt_ measurement of the amount of electricity used within one second

7. _Converter_ a device that switches direct current to alternating current

8. _Direct Current_ type of electric current that flows in only one direction

9. _Conductor_ opposite of nonconductor

10. _Fuse_ a device that is designed to prevent an excessive amount of electrical current from passing through a circuit

11. _Rectifier_ a device that switches alternating current to direct current

12. _Grounding_ term that means the electrical current is safely carried away from you

13. _Insulator_ a material that prevents the flow of electricity

14. _Alternating Current_ a rapid or interrupted current that switches direction

15. _Circuit Breaker_ a 'switch' that shuts off the flow of electricity in the event of an overload

16. _Fuse Box_ another name for a circuit breaker box

17. _Complete Electric Current_ electric current is described as the flow of positive and negative electric currents flowing through a generating source and ending where they started

# ELECTRICITY | WORD SEARCH

F T G X E P R X F Q J I L C N
H H N O F T S E M S N C U F X
T D I B M M E C C S J J C N L
G F T E P C R L U T E H N B W
R D A S E J U L P R I T C A S
O S N U S R A F E M C F T O Q
U Z R F A T E T U E O T I S I
N T E L O P R P R S S C D E G
D R T R F E M I M W E M H O R
I X L G V L D T T A W O L I K
N A A N A M P E R E I R V R E
G C O N D U C T O R R L O G T
Z C Q L Z X H O S V L K L M V
Q S C M M Y L W M W Z J T I X
R E K A E R B T I U C R I C M

# SKIN TYPES

pg. 745

**Describe the following:**

Normal Skin: smooth, moist, soft, with a healthy glow, free of blemishes

Oily Skin: textural appearance, large pores, shine with comedones/papules. or both, shiny, possible acne

Dry Skin: very small to no pores, shine-free, taut or rough feel. Fine lines + wrinkles

Combination Skin: two types, oily in the T-zone, smooth/rough texture, scaly appearance on outer perimeter (cheeks + hairline)

**Explain the proper treatments for each of the skin types.**

| | |
|---|---|
| NORMAL | Preserve |
| OILY | Control the flow of sebum; reduce appearance of pores |
| DRY | use hydrating products to nourish and prevent premature aging |
| COMBINATION | specialized regimen to treat 2 |

**List other skin type considerations:** pg. 747

Acne _____    Aging _____

Sensitive _____    sun-damaged/hyper-pigmented

Couperose _____    Dehydrated _____

228

# MASSAGE MANIPULATIONS

## Facial Treatment Procedure pg. 762-763

| DESCRIPTION OF TECHNIQUE | EFFECT |
|---|---|
|  **Effleurage:** Gliding, stroking, circular movements, light or no pressure light, slow, consistent motion | relaxing gentle |
|  **Petrissage:** Kneading, lifting or grasping | Provides deep stimulation to the muscle |
|  **Friction:** deep rubbing, rolling or wringing with pressure | glandular and stimulate circulation |
|  **Percussion / Tapotement:** short, light tapping or slapping movements. flexible fingers in rapid successions. ☆hacking movements. used for shoulders and the back. | provides most stimulation |
| 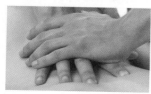 **Vibration:** rapid shaking movement, virtical movement | Very stimulating, should be done towards end of treatment |

## Motor Nerve Points

List the 4 facial motor nerve points that are effected by a facial massage. pg.

1. temporal
2. Zygomatic
3. Buccal
4. Mandibular

# HAIR REMOVAL

The definition for **Hirsutism** can be located on page ___768___; it lists
__hypertrichosis__, as another name.

The definition is:
__extreme hairiness / excessive growth of hair, some__
__uncommon areas of the face and body__

In reference to removing hair from the follicle, in what ways does tweezing differ from waxing?
__tweezing pulls individual hair strands; pulled in the direction of__
__growth; used for small areas__

Why would you choose tweezing over waxing as a form of hair removal?

__eliminate possibility of irritation__

Complete the following statements. Then use an orangewood stick and a pencil to draw
each point on the diagram.

**POINT A:** __Inside__ corner of the eye, remove any hair __outside__ the line.
**POINT B:** __Highest__ part of the brow, slightly outside the __iris__ of the eye.
**POINT C:** Located at the __end__ of brow, diagonally from the corner of the __nose__
to the outer corner of the __eye__.

# EYEBROW DESIGN | Using crayons, colored pencils, etc. draw complementary eyebrows.

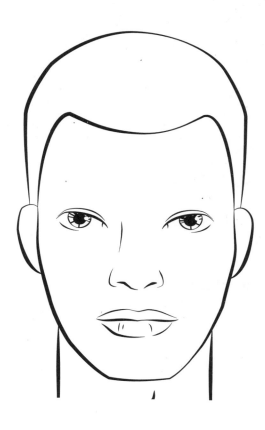

# WAXING | Do not wax if: Client has

1. irritated skin, open cuts, warts, moles, sunburned skin, recent scar tissue, recent skin grafts, tattoos, body piercings, fever blisters or cold sores

2. swelling, pus or inflammation of the pustules or papules of the skin

3. a chronic skin diseases, eczema or psoriasis

4. using or taking prescription meds that thins the skin, Meds will contribute to excessive peeling

5. had a microdermabrasion service in the past 90 days

6. had a Chemical Peel or Botox injections within 72 hours

7. had recent facial surgery or laser treatment

8. taking any medication for an autoimmune disease.

# MAKEUP APPLICATION ESSENTIALS

Skin Care

**Give examples of the following:**

Primary Colors: Red, Yellow, Blue

Secondary Colors: Orange, Green, Violet

Tertiary Colors: Yellow-green, Red-orange, Blue-violet, etc.

Complementary Colors: Red; Green, Blue, Orange ; yellow/violet

**Using the boxes below, experiment with colors by creating examples of each:**

| WARM COLORS | | | |
|---|---|---|---|

| COOL COLORS | | | |
|---|---|---|---|

**Describe the following makeup finishes:**

| FINISH | DESCRIPTION | USES |
|---|---|---|
| Matte | no shine, may be opaque or translucent | |
| Shiny | gloss or gleaming appearance | |
| Metallic | highly reflective; not transparent may be considered bright | |
| Opaque | unclear | |
| Translucent | lightly fogged | |
| Transparent | | |

# EYECOLOR

**What color eyeshadow(s) would you choose to complement each eye color? Fill in the shaded boxes; then using makeup, colored pencils, crayons, etc., 'apply' the appropriate eyeshadow color(s)**

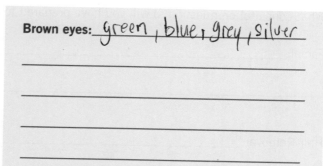

**Brown eyes:** green, blue, grey, silver

**Blue eyes:** gold, peach, copper, mauve, plum, taupe, camel

**Green eyes:** copper, rust, pink, plum, mauve, purple

**Hazel eyes:** earth tones, chestnut, bronze, gold, olive, emerald, silver, purple, maroon

# DEVELOPING YOUR SKIN CARE COMMUNICATION AND SOLUTION SKILLS

What consultation question(s) will you have prepared to ask your Guest for the following:

Facial:_____

_____

Hair Removal:_____

_____

Makeup Application:_____

_____

_____

Your Guest wants a corrective treatment to improve their acne-prone skin. How would you analyze their skin and select the appropriate treatment(s) and/or products?

_____

_____

Your Guest has never received a professional makeup application. What would you tell them to expect?

_____

_____

Your Guest is pregnant, retaining fluid, and asking for a leg wax. What would your recommendation(s) be?

_____

_____

## SERVICE RECOMMENDATIONS

Skin Care treatment options:_____

_____

Makeup options:_____

_____

## MAINTENANCE RECOMMENDATIONS

When discussing a maintenance routine with your Guest, how often will you suggest they rebook for the following services:

Facial: _____

Hair Removal: _____

Makeup Application: _____

## PRODUCT RECOMMENDATIONS FOR AT HOME USE

Skin Care:_____

_____

Makeup:_____

_____

# MY NEED TO KNOW notes:

# WORKSHOP
# standards

|  | MET | SKILL |
|---|---|---|

## Safety and Infection Control:

Disinfect work station *(before and after each service)*
Set up work station with required, clean service tools
Apply gloves
Use of disinfected or disposable implements

## Consultation:

Skin Analysis: ☐normal ☐dry ☐oily ☐combination ☐clogged pores ☐abrasions
Drape: neck strip, towel, cape, towel, head band / hair covering
*(eye pads over eyes for facial procedure only)*
Cleanse area to be treated

## Facial Procedure:

Remove cleansing cream thoroughly from face
Apply toner; analyze skin for abrasions, oil, flakiness or clogged pores
Apply warm, moist towel prior to exfoliation
Apply then remove exfoliant
Apply massage cream using proper massage techniques:
☐Effleurage ☐Petrissage ☐Percussion ☐Friction ☐Vibration
Remove massage cream
Apply mask and allow to set; remove mask
Apply moisturizer
End with light massage of the face, neck and shoulders

## Hair Removal Procedures: *Eyebrow*

Waxing:
  Measure and design desired eyebrow shape
  Test temperature of wax
  Apply thin layer of wax in direction of hair growth
  Apply wax strip over wax area, gently pressing in direction of hair growth
  Hold skin taut; remove wax strip in the opposite direction of hair growth
Tweezing:
  Measure and design desired eyebrow shape
  Remove tweezers from sanitary container
  Hold skin taut; remove hair in direction of growth

## Finishing of Service:

Complete service according to manufacturer's post-treatment recommendations
Proceed with makeup application *(if desired or applicable)*
Dispose of all used materials
Recommend at-home maintenance products

# SITUATIONAL SCENARIOS

**1.** Your facial Guest has just returned from a vacation. You notice during the skin analysis that her skin is tan. Her tan skin is the result of the effects of ultraviolet rays that increased the amount of:

    **a)** Sebum in her skin
    **b)** Keratin in her skin
    **c)** Milia in her skin
    **d)** Melanin in her skin

**2.** Your Guest, Fran, arrived for her facial treatment. During the consultation, Fran asks you what can be done about the age spots on her face. What would you suggest?

    **a)** To use a color lightener on the skin to bleach the dark spots
    **b)** To stay out of the sun and use daily sun protection at all times
    **c)** To change her daily cleansing routine to products that will remove the excessive oil from the skin
    **d)** To avoid products that have a fragrance

**3.** When performing your skin analysis on Wendy, a regular Guest, you notice that since her last visit she has developed a dark spot on her forehead. How should you proceed?

    **a)** Recommend that Wendy see a medical professional
    **b)** Ignore the spot, because Wendy is self-conscious of it
    **c)** Explain to Wendy the spot is some type of skin pigmentation, and she shouldn't worry about it
    **d)** During the facial, use a strong exfoliant on the spot

**4.** Your Guest Bill, would like to know the difference between lathering cleansers versus non-lathering cleansers. How would you explain?

    **a)** Non-lathering cleansers are used primarily to remove makeup; whereas lathering cleansers are used to cleanse dirt and debris from the skin
    **b)** Non-lathering cleansers are for use on oily skin or acne-prone skin because they will not clog pores
    **c)** Lathering cleansers produce a foam consistency and are best suited for combination to oily skin; whereas, non-lathering cleansers have a cream consistency and are best suited for dry skin
    **d)** Lathering cleansers are gentler to the skin, providing a hydrating and softening effect; whereas, non-lathering cleansers are a professional product with a creamy consistency used for deep cleaning during a facial

**5.** Your Guest has acne and is requesting a waxing service. Prior to providing the service you must determine if your Guest is taking or using any medication for their skin condition. Why is this question important to ask?

    **a)** Hard wax can only be used on a Guest who is currently taking medication
    **b)** Acne skin retains fluid so the wax will not come off
    **c)** Certain acne skin medication will thin the skin, which can cause excessive removal of skin cells
    **d)** It is not a concern and should not be addressed with the Guest

**6.** During a consultation, your Guest asked if there is a treatment that can be used to reduce the amount of oil on his face. What would you recommend?

    **a)** Clay mask
    **b)** Cream mask
    **c)** Paraffin wax mask
    **d)** Modelage mask

**7.** James has arrived for a pre-booked facial massage appointment. Before beginning the facial you review his history; a note was added that James prefers a soothing facial massage. On what type of massage movement should you focus?

    **a)** Effleurage
    **b)** Petrissage
    **c)** Vibration
    **d)** Percussion

**8.** Amanda has booked a makeup appointment for the morning of her wedding. She arrives at the salon with a freshly cleansed, toned and moisturized face, but she has a blemish on her forehead and some dark circles under her eyes. To cover the blemish and reduce the discoloration around the eyes, you will need to apply a concealer that is _____.

    **a)** Lighter than the skin tone
    **b)** The same as the skin tone
    **c)** Heavier than the skin tone
    **d)** Darker than the skin tone

**9.** During your skin analysis, you identify that your Guest has very small pores, the skin appears taut and is slightly flakey in some areas. But, in the nose, chin, and forehead, the pores are larger, with some blemishes and oil. What type of skin does your Guest have?

    **a)** Dry
    **b)** Oily
    **c)** Couperose
    **d)** Combination

**10.** Regina, a newly acquired Guest, received her first professional facial in the salon. The next day she called to say that her skin is breaking out and appears to be red and irritated. What might be the cause of Regina's complaint?

    **a)** Incorrect product selection
    **b)** Overstimulation during facial massage
    **c)** Overly aggressive extraction process
    **d)** All of the above

**11.** During the consultation with your Guest, they ask you to remove (tweeze or wax) hair from a mole. What should you do?

    **a)** Use hard wax and remove the hair
    **b)** Explain that for their safety you are unable to remove the hair
    **c)** Remove the hair, but wear sterile gloves
    **d)** Ask the salon owner for permission

**12.** During a skin consultation, you learn the following information about your Guest: Mia is 24 years old, just had a baby and is nursing, and this is her first facial. What do you need to consider for the facial?

    **a)** Avoid massage manipulations, you do not want to increase the circulation
    **b)** Recommend Mia receive medical permission prior to receiving the facial
    **c)** Use pH-balanced products
    **d)** No additional steps are necessary

# practical PREP

*Each skill will be checked by your Educator and feedback will be provided.*
*Met Skill = 1 point / Not Met Skill = 0 points*

**POINTS**

## Safety and Disinfection:

Disinfects work station *(before and after each service)*
Station set up with required tools
Uses disinfected or disposable implements
Applies gloves
Performs skin analysis
Drapes for skin care (facial) procedure
Cleanses area(s) to be treated
**Feedback:**

## Facial Procedure:

Removes cleanser completely and gently *(no pulling)*
Applies toner
Analyzes skin for abrasions, oil, flakiness or clogged pores
Applies exfoliant gently to face
Removes exfoliant
Applies massage cream to entire face
Demonstrates proper massage techniques, maintaining constant contact:
    Effleurage
    Petrissage
    Percussion
    Friction
    Vibration
Removes massage cream completely without pulling skin
Applies toner / astringent safely
Applies mask, allows to set
Removes mask and all residue
Applies moisturizer and ends with light massage of the face, neck and shoulders
**Feedback:**

## Hair Removal Procedure – *Eyebrow*:

**Waxing / Tweezing: mock demonstration of both removal procedures**
Measures and designs desired eyebrow shape
    Waxing: Tests temperature of wax; applies thin layer of wax in direction of hair growth
    Waxing: Applies wax strip over wax area; gently presses in direction of hair growth
Holds skin taut
    Waxing: Removes wax strip in opposite direction of hair growth
    Tweezing: Removes hair in same direction of hair growth
Applies post-wax product to treated area
**Feedback:**

# SKIN CARE
## STATE BOARD THEORY REVIEW

1. A chronic inflammation of the sebaceous glands:

   a) seborrhea     b) acne     c) dermatitis     d) anhidrosis

2. The final stage of the Human Immunodeficiency Virus:

   a) AIDS     b) cancer     c) melanoma     d) hepatitis

3. In a/an _____ current, the flow of electricity reverses direction:

   a) alternating     b) direct     c) normal     d) steady

4. Dermatitis Venenata is an allergic reaction caused by exposure to certain:

   a) products     b) heat     c) cold air     d) water

5. The subcutaneous tissue is _____ tissue found beneath the dermis:

   a) liquid     b) muscular     c) protective     d) fatty

6. A congenital disorder characterized by the complete or partial absence of pigment in the skin, hair and eyes:

   a) eczema     b) melanoma     c) rosacea     d) albinism

7. In the visible spectrum of light, _____ of visible light rays account for natural sunlight:

   a) 10%     b) 35%     c) 50%     d) 85%

8. _____ is a lack of perspiration due to an underactive sudoriferous gland:

   a) Hyperhidrosis     b) Bromhidrosis     c) Anhidrosis     d) None of the above

9. An anode is typically designed to do the following:

   a) decrease blood flow     b) reduce redness or inflammation     c) harden skin tissue, closing pores     d) all of the above

10. An _____ is an agent that prevents or reduces infection by eliminating or decreasing the growth of microorganisms:

   a) antiseptic     b) staphylococci     c) flagella     d) contamination

# SKIN CARE
## STATE BOARD THEORY REVIEW

11. MRSA is the acronym for:

a) Motor Resistant Staphylococcus Aureus

b) Muscular Resistant Staphylococcus Aureus

c) Methicillin Resistant Staphylococcus Aureus

d) Melanoma Resistant Staphylococcus Aureus

12. The aorta is the largest _____ of the body:

a) vein

b) capillary

c) artery

d) atrium

13. The top chambers of the heart:

a) ventricles

b) arteries

c) valves

d) atrium

14. Also known as blackheads, these hair follicles contain hardened and darkened sebum:

a) comedo

b) milia

c) pore

d) sebaceous cyst

15. _____ is the mildest type of skin cancer:

a) Squamous cell carcinoma

b) Basal cell carcinoma

c) Malignant melanoma

d) Melanoma

16. The outermost protective layer of the skin containing many small nerve endings, but no blood vessels:

a) epidermis

b) dermis

c) stratum germinativum

d) true layer

17. The middle portion of a muscle:

a) belly

b) insertion

c) origin

d) base

18. A type of disinfectant that kills bacteria:

a) bactericidal

b) pesticidal

c) sterilizer

d) sanitizer

19. _____ nourishes and supplies oxygen to the body:

a) Nerves

b) Blood

c) Sebum

d) Keratin

20. One of the six functions of the skin that aids in its ability to stretch and return:

a) heat regulation

b) absorption

c) secretion

d) excretion

# SKIN CARE
## STATE BOARD THEORY REVIEW

21. HIV, Hepatitis B, and Hepatitis C are common types of diseases caused by a:

a) microbe     b) cocci     c) bloodborne pathogen     d) flagella

22. The sudoriferous gland disorder that causes foul-smelling perspiration:

a) hyperhidrosis     b) bromhidrosis     c) anhidrosis     d) miliaria rubra

23. Bulla is a large blister containing:

a) opaque sebum     b) blood and lymph     c) clear, watery fluid     d) pus

24. The muscle that pumps blood through the circulatory system:

a) cardiac muscle     b) stomach muscle     c) lung     d) lymphatic muscle

25. Cathode is typically designed to do the following:

a) increase blood flow     b) soften skin     c) penetrate alkaline solutions into the skin     d) all of the above

26. The basic unit of all living matter:

a) cell     b) tissue     c) matter     d) bulla

27. Circuit Breaker is a 'switch' that _____ the flow of electricity at the first signs of an overload:

a) manually increases     b) automatically surges     c) manually shuts off     d) automatically shuts off

28. A panel or device that automatically stops the flow of electricity:

a) fuse     b) circuit breaker box     c) conductor     d) amplifier

29. This system transports blood and lymph throughout the body:

a) nervous     b) respiratory     c) circulatory     d) excretory

30. Long-lasting or recurring disorders or diseases:

a) contagious     b) community     c) acute     d) chronic

31. The main artery that supplies the head and neck with oxygenated blood:

a) thoracic     b) carpal     c) tibial     d) common carotid artery

# SKIN CARE
## STATE BOARD THEORY REVIEW

32. The flow of positive and negative electric currents through a conductor and back to the generating source:

a) electrical track      b) circuit path      c) alternating currents      **d) complete electric current**

33. An infection of the eyes that is highly contagious:

a) conjunctivitis      **b) pink eye**      c) glaucoma      **d) both a and b**

34. Metal, copper, and water are _____ of electricity:

**a) conductors**      b) nonconductors      c) insulators      d) amps

35. Identify a preventative measure to limit the effects of contact dermatitis:

**a) wear gloves when handling chemicals**      b) use moisturizers to help keep the skin moist      c) clean and disinfect your work area before and after servicing each Guest      **d) all of the above**

36. A device that switches DC to AC; the opposite of a rectifier:

**a) converter**      b) circuit      c) conductor      d) volt

37. Dry or moist patches of skin that are painful and itchy:

**a) eczema**      b) asteatosis      c) acne      d) steatoma

38. An inflammation of the skin:

a) dermatitis      b) pustule      c) miliaria rubra      **d) rosacea**

39. Ampere or amp is the unit that measures the _____ of an electric current:

a) force      b) wattage      **c) strength**      d) speed

40. Tumors may penetrate into the dermis and be:

a) benign      b) malignant      c) liquid      **d) both a and b**

41. A small, uneven pigmented spot on the skin's surface:

a) papule      **b) mole**      c) verruca      d) wheal

42. _____ is the underlying or inner layer of skin:

a) Corium layer      b) Epidermis      **c) Dermis**      d) Subcutaneous tissue

# SKIN CARE
## STATE BOARD THEORY REVIEW

43. The branch of medicine dealing with the skin and its diseases:

   a) dermatology     b) myology     c) histology     d) endocrinology

44. The system that digests food and breaks it down into nutrients:

   a) circulatory     b) endocrine     c) integumentary     d) digestive

45. A current that flows in one direction:

   a) sporadic current     b) alternating current     c) direct current     d) all of the above

46. The process of destroying most pathogenic bacteria and toxins on nonporous surfaces:

   a) sanitation     b) sterilization     c) disinfection     d) contamination

47. The sudoriferous and sebaceous glands are known as:

   a) endocrine glands     b) sensory glands     c) ductless glands     d) duct glands

48. A closed, abnormally developed sac containing fluids or morbid matter:

   a) crust     b) keloid     c) cyst     d) fissure

49. A spongy bone located between both eye sockets:

   a) nasal     b) ethmoid     c) parietal     d) occipital

50. What is the device that switches AC to DC:

   a) converter     b) inverter     c) rectifier     d) amplifier

51. What system includes ductless glands that regulate hormone production:

   a) digestive     b) endocrine     c) reproductive     d) circulatory

52. This skin layer is the outer layer:

   a) reticular     b) epidermis     c) dermis     d) papillary

53. Effleurage is a massage technique that involves constant movement of light, slow gliding and:

   a) stroking     b) kneading     c) shaking     d) tapping

**54. Excoriation is:**

a) a scraping of the skin    b) a large blister    c) cracks in the skin    d) a scar formed after healing

**55. Excretion disperses perspiration, which aids in:**

a) maintaining a healthy temperature    b) protecting the skin    c) moisturizing the skin    d) sending messages to the body's nerve receptors

**56. This system is comprised of the kidneys, liver, skin, large intestine, and lungs:**

a) endocrine    b) respiratory    c) excretory    d) digestive

**57. This massage technique provides deep stimulation to the muscles using a rolling, rubbing or wringing movement:**

a) effleurage    b) petrissage    c) percussion    d) friction

**58. Which salon disinfectant can destroy fungi:**

a) fungicidal    b) virucidal    c) bactericidal    d) tuberculocidal

**59. This prevents an excessive amount of electricity from passing through a circuit:**

a) fuse    b) extension cord    c) amp    d) ohm

**60. A device that links to the main source of electricity:**

a) electric meter    b) surge protector    c) fuse box    d) grounding wire

**61. The six functions of skin are protection, absorption, secretion, excretion, sensation, and:**

a) tanning    b) penetration    c) heat regulation    d) reducing muscle tension

**62. _____ is an iron supporting protein, that gives blood color:**

a) Erythrocytes    b) Leukocytes    c) Platelets    d) Hemoglobin

**63. A bloodborne virus that can cause inflammation of the liver and is characterized by jaundice, fever, and abdominal pain:**

a) hepatitis    b) HIV    c) AIDS    d) herpes

64. Commonly referred to as a cold sore, the technical term for a contagious skin disorder characterized as an eruption of a vesicle situated on an inflamed base:

a) herpes simplex      b) miliaria rubra      c) impetigo      d) rosacea

65. The virus that causes Acquired Immune Deficiency Syndrome:

a) HPV      b) HIV      c) AIDS      d) hepatitis

66. Histology is the study of:

a) muscles and their functions      b) the skin, its structure, functions, diseases, and treatments      c) the functions and activities performed by the body      d) the microscopic anatomy of cells and tissues of plants and animals

67. An over-abundance of perspiration:

a) hyperhidrosis      b) bromhidrosis      c) anhidrosis      d) miliaria rubra

68. An excessive hairiness in those parts of the body where terminal hair does not normally occur:

a) hypertrichosis      b) albinism      c) hyperpigmentation      d) impetigo

69. A contagious bacterial infection characterized by open lesions found by the nose and/or mouth:

a) acne rosacea      b) dermatitis      c) hepatitis      d) impetigo

70. The insertion is attached to the:

a) center part of the muscle      b) immovable part of the bone      c) movable portion of the bone      d) center part of the bone

71. Also known as an insulator, this material prevents the flow of electricity:

a) metal      b) nonconductor      c) conductor      d) volt

72. This unit measures 1,000 watts of electrical power used within one second:

a) kilowatt      b) volt      c) ohm      d) milliampere

73. _____ diseases begin abruptly and can be severe or painful, then subside after a short period of time:

a) Chronic      b) Acute      c) Skin      d) Sebaceous Gland

74. Commonly referred to as a birthmark:

a) chloasma    b) nevus    c) wheal    d) macule

75. Light that is not visible to the naked eye:

a) visible light    b) red light    c) invisible light    d) blue light

76. The process of using a Galvanic current to force a water-based soluble solution into the skin:

a) microdermabrasion    b) chemical peels    c) light therapy    d) iontophoresis

77. _____ is thickened or hardened areas of skin caused by friction:

a) Keratoma    b) Verruca    c) Mole    d) Nevus

78. The _____ is comprised of skin and serves as a protective covering:

a) nervous system    b) integumentary system    c) circulatory system    d) excretory system

79. Lesions are grouped into which categories:

a) temporary and permanent    b) primary and secondary    c) acute and chronic    d) superficial and severe

80. Leukoderma is a skin disorder characterized by:

a) dark patches    b) light patches    c) brown patches    d) red patches

81. Lymph is a clear, _____ fluid that circulates throughout the lymphatic system:

a) very red    b) non-white    c) slightly yellow    d) deep blue

82. The lymphatic / immune system develops:

a) nutrients    b) cells    c) immunities    d) pathogens

83. A discoloration that is normally flat, small and can vary in color, shapes and size:

a) melanin    b) macule    c) tumor    d) vesicle

84. A dark pigmented tumor typically associated with skin cancer:

a) macule    b) melanoma    c) leukoderma    d) impetigo

85. The most dangerous form of skin cancer is:

a) malignant melanoma    b) basal cell carcinoma    c) squamous cell carcinoma    d) non-melanoma carcinoma

# SKIN CARE
## STATE BOARD THEORY REVIEW

86. Microcurrents are low level electrical currents that are similar to the electrical currents produced by:

   a) electrical equipment   b) the human body   c) weather   d) water

87. The process by which a cell duplicates into two daughter cells:

   a) mitosis   b) nevus   c) cancer   d) skin tag

88. Miliaria rubra is also known as:

   a) prickly heat   b) heat rash   c) birthmark   d) both a and b

89. Less than 1/1000 of an ampere, a common strength used in facials, is known as:

   a) watt   b) milliampere   c) kilowatt   d) volt

90. Small, white keratin-filled bumps or cysts that are enclosed within the epidermis:

   a) milia   b) comedones   c) blackheads   d) dry skin

91. Keratinization is most active in this layer, as the cells are forced upward and flatten due to the introduction of the protein, keratin:

   a) stratum lucidum   b) stratum granulosum   c) stratum corneum   d) stratum germinativum

92. A unit for measuring the resistance of an electric current:

   a) ohm   b) volt   c) ampere   d) amp

93. This system supports the skeletal system:

   a) circulatory   b) digestive   c) endocrine   d) muscular

94. The Nervous System is comprised of:

   a) stomach, intestines, mouth and glands   b) kidney, liver, skin, large intestines and lungs   c) brain, spinal cord and nerves   d) blood, blood vessels and the heart

95. Neurology is the scientific study of the:

   a) nervous system   b) muscular system   c) skeletal system   d) circulatory system

96. An example of a non-striated involuntary muscle:

   a) arm muscle   b) forehead muscle   c) corrugated muscle   d) stomach muscle

97. These nerve fibers carry messages to the brain and/or spinal cord to produce movement:

   a) motor   b) secretory   c) sensory   d) mixed

# SKIN CARE
## STATE BOARD THEORY REVIEW

98. The pore of an open comedone appears _____ due to the sebum being exposed to the environment:

a) white      b) black      c) red      d) clear

99. Separate body structures that perform a specific function; lungs are an example:

a) cells      b) tissues      c) organs      d) system

100. The thyroid gland controls how quickly the body burns energy, makes proteins and:

a) regulates the body temperature      b) regulates growth and reproduction      c) releases hormones in response to stress      d) controls how sensitive the body is to other hormones

101. The origin is attached to the _____ portion of bones:

a) immovable      b) movable      c) center      d) rotating

102. Pus is most likely to be found in:

a) vesicles      b) scars      c) macules      d) pustules

103. What layer contains some of the following: small blood vessels, melanin, dermal papillae, tactile corpuscles:

a) stratum corneum      b) stratum germinativum      c) papillary layer      d) subcutaneous layer

104. An example of a papule:

a) blister      b) pimple      c) burn      d) birthmark

105. Percussion is a massage technique that involves which type of movement:

a) light tapping      b) slapping      c) both a and b      d) neither a nor b

106. Petrissage is a massage technique that involves:

a) gliding, stroking or circular movements      b) kneading, lifting or grasping movements      c) deep rubbing, rolling or wringing movements      d) rapid shaking movements

107. Tiny color-free particles in the blood that are responsible for the clotting or coagulation of blood:

a) platelets      b) thrombocytes      c) leukocytes      d) both a and b

108. Polarity is the property of having _____ poles of an electric current:

a) positive and negative      b) single and double      c) beginning and end      d) small and large

109. This function of the skin guards the skin from UV rays, extreme weather conditions, bacterial infections and injuries:

a) absorption      b) secretion      c) excretion      d) protection

# SKIN CARE
## STATE BOARD THEORY REVIEW

110. The living jelly-like part of a cell:

a) cell membrane    b) nucleus    c) protoplasm    d) cell wall

111. Osteology is the study of:

a) muscles    b) nerves    c) infections    d) bones

112. The system that is comprised of the organs necessary to reproduce:

a) reproductive    b) endocrine    c) respiratory    d) integumentary

113. This system contains the organs that help to process air:

a) reproductive    b) endocrine    c) respiratory    d) integumentary

114. The dermal layer that contains a majority of the skin's structures, such as nerve fibers, hair papilla, fat cells, blood and lymph capillaries, oil and sweat glands, and the arrector pili muscles:

a) papillary    b) reticular    c) subcutaneous    d) epidermis

115. These glands are located everywhere on the body, with the exception of the palms of the hands and soles of the feet:

a) sebaceous    b) sudoriferous    c) sweat    d) adrenaline

116. The chemical process that reduces surface pathogens but will not kill bacteria:

a) disinfection    b) sanitation    c) purification    d) sterilization

117. Rosacea is a _____ skin disorder:

a) chronic    b) acute    c) carcinogenic    d) malignant

118. _____ provides moisture to the skin and hair, lubricating and helping to prevent the skin from wrinkling and/or hair from breaking:

a) Hormone    b) Sebum    c) Melanin    d) Perspiration

119. Wheal is also known as:

a) vesicle    b) urticaria    c) macule    d) ulcer

120. This function of the skin aids in maintaining the skin's moisture and elasticity:

a) protection    b) heat regulation    c) secretion    d) sensation

121. The function of the skin that includes the stimulation and reaction to touch, heat, cold, pressure, and pain:

a) protection    b) sensation    c) absorption    d) excretion

# SKIN CARE
## STATE BOARD THEORY REVIEW

122. _____ are responsible for our recognizing touch, cold, heat, sight, hearing, taste, smell, pain and pressure:

a) Sensory nerves    b) Motor nerves    c) Mixed nerves    d) Efferent nerves

123. The physical foundation of the body; composed of 206 bones:

a) muscular system    b) endocrine system    c) skeletal system    d) integumentary system

124. _____ is more serious than Basal Cell Carcinoma and is characterized by red, scaly patches or open sores that may bleed or crust:

a) Malignant melanoma    b) Basal cell carcinoma    c) Squamous cell carcinoma    d) Mildest cell carcinoma

125. What is the most effective level of infection control:

a) sanitation    b) sterilization    c) disinfectant    d) antiseptic

126. This layer consists of tightly-packed, scale-like hardened cells that are continuously shed and replaced by new cells:

a) stratum lucidum    b) stratum granulosum    c) stratum corneum    d) stratum germinativum

127. Stratum Germinativum is basically known as the _____ layer of the epidermis:

a) clear    b) mature    c) birth    d) horny

128. The _____ layer is made up of clear cells, which allow light to pass through:

a) stratum lucidum    b) stratum granulosum    c) stratum corneum    d) stratum germinativum

129. Stratum Spinosum is the layer where the cells develop tiny spines that assist in:

a) the production of melanin    b) cushioning the skin    c) protecting the skin against the harmful rays of the sun    d) binding all cells tightly together

130. This type of voluntary muscle moves the fingers:

a) non-striated    b) striated    c) fibrous    d) flat

131. The ability of a product to produce favorable results:

a) SDS    b) immunity    c) efficacy    d) level

132. These tube-like ducts begin in the dermis, extend into the epidermis and excrete sweat:

a) hair follicles    b) sebaceous glands    c) sudoriferous glands    d) skin pores

133. _____ diseases are often due to over-functioning or under-functioning internal glands or organs:

   a) Digestive          b) Muscular          c) Skin          d) Systemic

134. _____ involves short, light tapping or slapping movements:

   a) Effluerage          b) Tapotement          c) Petrissage          d) Vibration

135. The Pituitary Gland is responsible for growth, metabolism, sexual organ functions and:

   a) breast milk production          b) blood pressure          c) contractions during childbirth          d) all of the above

136. A beneficial effect of Tesla High Frequency Current:

   a) promotes skin tissue healing          b) reduces sinus congestion          c) aids in absorption of products          d) all of the above

137. Epithelial, nerve, muscular, connective, and liquid are types of:

   a) organs          b) cells          c) tissues          d) systems

138. The salon disinfectant that is able to kill the bacteria that causes tuberculosis:

   a) tuberculocidal          b) fungicidal          c) virucidal          d) bactericidal

139. This permits blood to flow in one direction:

   a) valve          b) chamber          c) ventricle          d) atrium

140. Veins are _____, tube-like vessels that carry and keep the blood flowing in one direction to the heart:

   a) thin-walled          b) thick-walled          c) very tiny          d) large, thick

141. Ventricles are the thick-walled chambers on the _____ of the heart:

   a) top half          b) bottom half          c) upper half          d) outside

142. A verruca is commonly found on the:

   a) hands and feet          b) eyes and lips          c) elbows and back          d) ears and neck

143. A vesicle is a small elevated blister or sac filled with a _____, located within or directly below the epidermis:

   a) red fluid          b) dense fluid          c) white fluid          d) clear fluid

144. This massage technique involves the use of the tips of the fingers to produce a rapid shaking movement:

   a) effleurage          b) tapotement          c) petrissage          d) vibration

# SKIN CARE
## STATE BOARD THEORY REVIEW

145. Non-elevated, hyperpigmented spots that may form because of frequent sun exposure, heredity or hormonal changes:

    a) rosacea          b) leukoderma          c) vitiligo          **d) chloasma**

146. Tesla High Frequency Current is also known as:

    a) blue ray          b) white ray          c) infrared ray          **d) violet ray**

147. The salon disinfectant that is capable of destroying viruses:

    a) tuberculocidal          b) fungicidal          **c) virucidal**          d) bactericidal

148. The strength of a light bulb is measured in:

    a) volts          b) ohms          **c) watts**          d) amperes

149. Vitiligo is a skin disorder with irregularly-shaped _____ patches:

    a) brown          b) pink          **c) white**          d) black

150. The unit for measuring the force or pressure of an electric current:

    **a) volts**          b) ohms          c) watts          d) amperes

151. Shorter wavelengths have:

    a) more energy and more heat          b) less energy and less heat          c) less energy and more heat          **d) more energy and less heat**

152. Hives are an example of a/an:

    a) chloasma          b) excoriation          c) vesicle          d) wheal

153. Whiteheads are also known as:

    a) blackheads          b) vesicles          **c) closed comedones**          d) open comedones

154. Myology is the study of:

    a) skin          **b) muscles**          c) disease          d) microorganisms

155. Able to kill the bacteria pseudomonas aeruginosa:

    a) virucidal          b) fungicidal          c) tuberculocidal          **d) pseudomonacidal**

254

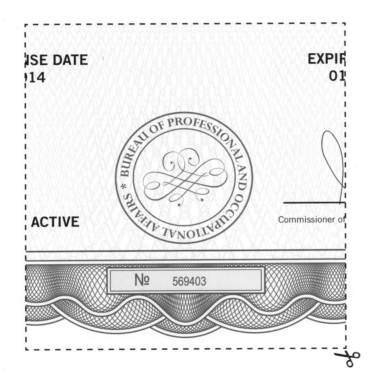

NSE DATE

EXPIR

)14

01

ACTIVE

BUREAU OF PROFESSIONAL AND OCCUPATIONAL AFFAIRS *

Commissioner of

№ 569403

# NAIL CARE

# SAFETY AND DISINFECTION

A. Phenols

B. Alcohol

C. Sodium Hypochlorite

D. Accelerated Hydrogen Peroxide

E. Chelating Soaps

F. Quaternary Ammonium Compounds

G. Lungs

1. __D__ based on a stabilized hydrogen peroxide and is non-toxic to the skin and environment

2. __A__ strong, high pH disinfectants

3. __G__ spongy respiratory organs that must be protected from dust and airborne chemicals

4. __C__ commonly known as bleach

5. __F__ a standard name for disinfectants

6. __B__ an extremely flammable, colorless liquid that evaporates quickly

7. __E__ help break down and remove the residue from foot soaks, scrubs and masks

# TOOLS AND PRODUCTS

**Circle the correct answer.**

1. A nail dehydrator is a semi-liquid solution applied first to the natural nail to help eliminate moisture. **TRUE / FALSE**

2. Curettes are wooden tools that are used to scoop and remove debris. **TRUE / FALSE**

3. Metal pushers are used to gently scrape the cuticle from the nail bed. **TRUE / FALSE**

4. Metal pushers are safe to use on infected skin. **TRUE / FALSE**

5. Nail wrap resins are a type of adhesive applied to nail fabrics. **TRUE / FALSE**

6. Cleansing soaks are a great way to cleanse and soften skin. **TRUE / FALSE**

7. Exfoliating scrubs are smooth lotions or gels that are massaged onto the foot and leg. **TRUE / FALSE**

8. Wooden pushers are made from softwoods. **TRUE / FALSE**

9. Wooden pushers are reusable. **TRUE / FALSE**

10. Nail rasps are metal tools that are typically used during pedicures to smooth and file the free edge. **TRUE / FALSE**

11. Monomer is a gel-like substance that is mixed with a powder to form an acrylic nail. **TRUE / FALSE**

12. Polymers are combined with an acrylic liquid to form an acrylic nail. **TRUE / FALSE**

13. Cuticle removers typically contain a low amount of sodium or potassium hydroxide. **TRUE / FALSE**

14. Callus softeners are not designed to be used directly on the skin. **TRUE / FALSE**

15. A scoop is used to move product from its original container to a dappen dish. **TRUE / FALSE**

# BONES OF THE ARM

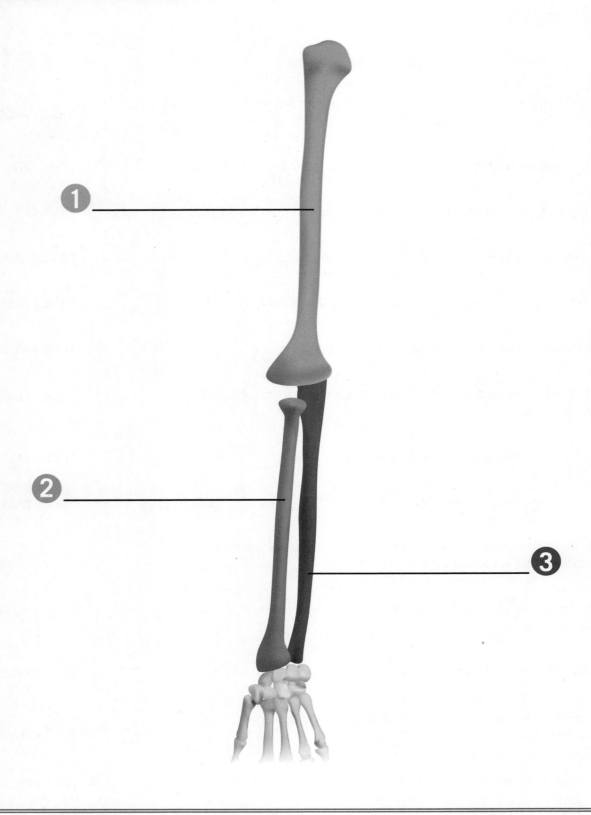

**1.** upper bone of the arm

**2.** outer smaller bone of the forearm

**3.** larger inner bone of the forearm

# BONES OF THE HAND

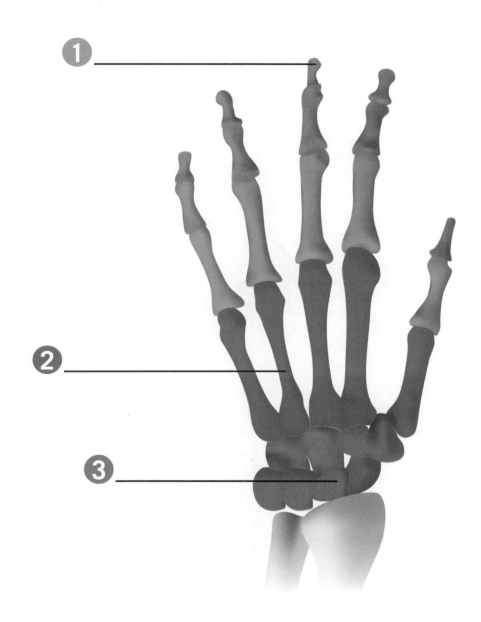

1 —————————————

2 —————————————

3 —————————————

**1.** also known as digits

**2.** 5 long bones that form the palm of the hand

**3.** 8 small bones that form the wrist

# BONES OF THE LEGS

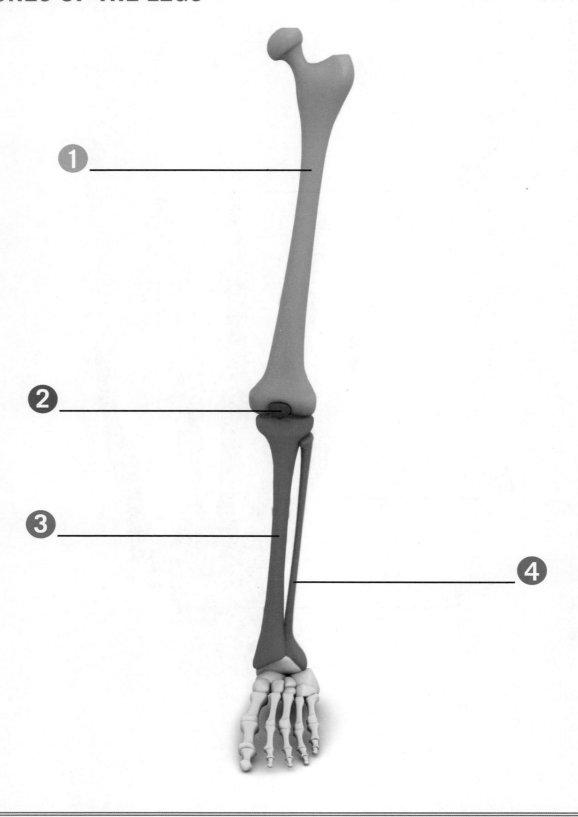

1 _____

2 _____

3 _____

4 _____

1. also known as the thigh bone

2. also known as the knee cap

3. also known as the shin bone

4. smaller of the 2 bones that
   form the lower leg

# BONES OF THE FEET

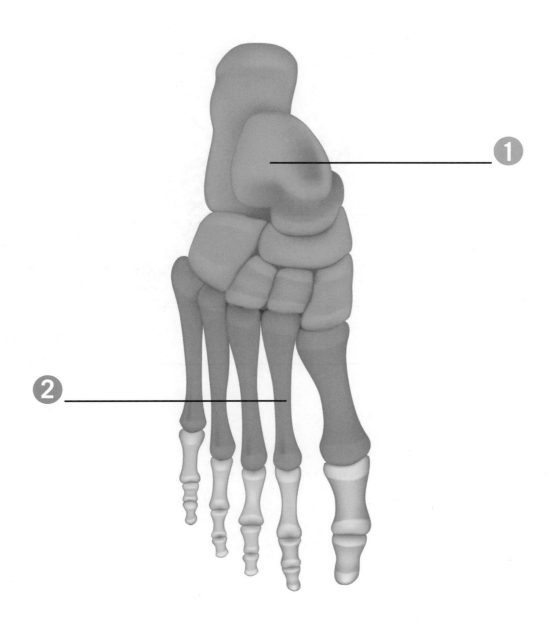

**1.** 7 bones that form the ankle    **2.** 5 bones that form the arch of the foot

# MUSCLES OF THE ARM

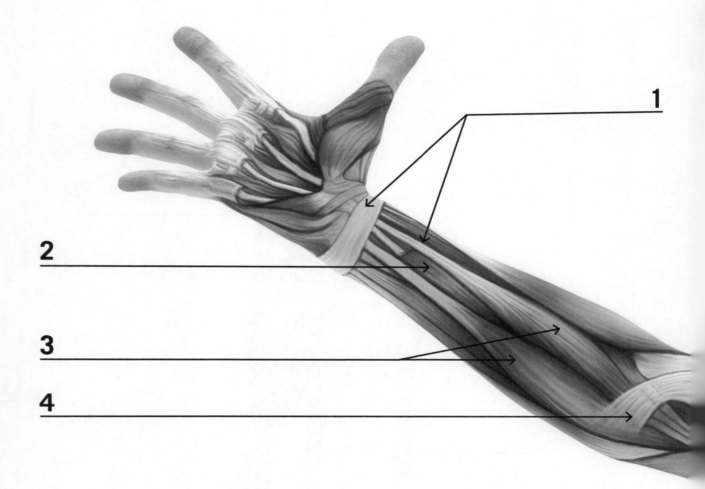

1

2

3

4

1. cause joints to straighten and body parts to stretch; these muscles make the wrist and fingers straighten out

2. turn the forearm and hand inward so the palm faces downward

3. cause the joints to bend and produce the bending and curling of the wrist and fingers

4. turn the forearm and hand outward so the palm faces upward

# MUSCLES OF THE HAND

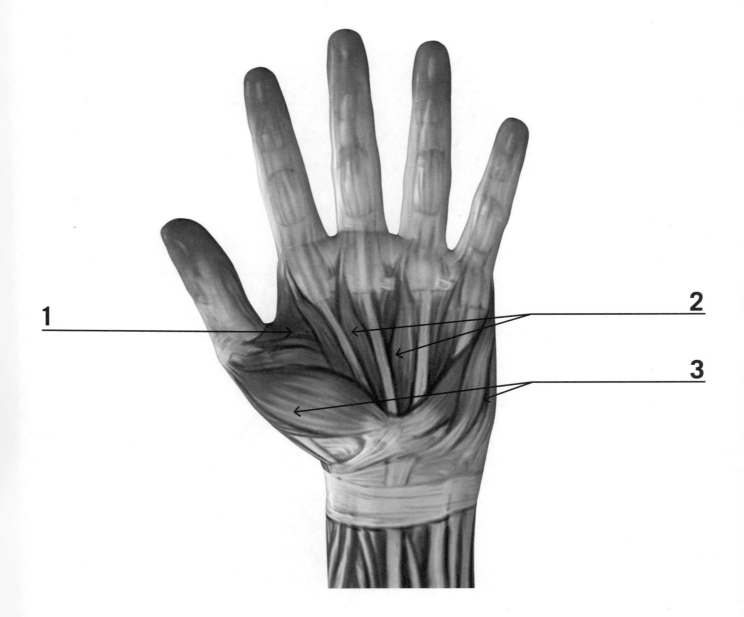

**1.** pull the fingers together

**2.** spread or separate the fingers

**3.** a group of adductor muscles, located in the palm, that draw the thumb toward the fingers

# MUSCLES OF THE LEGS

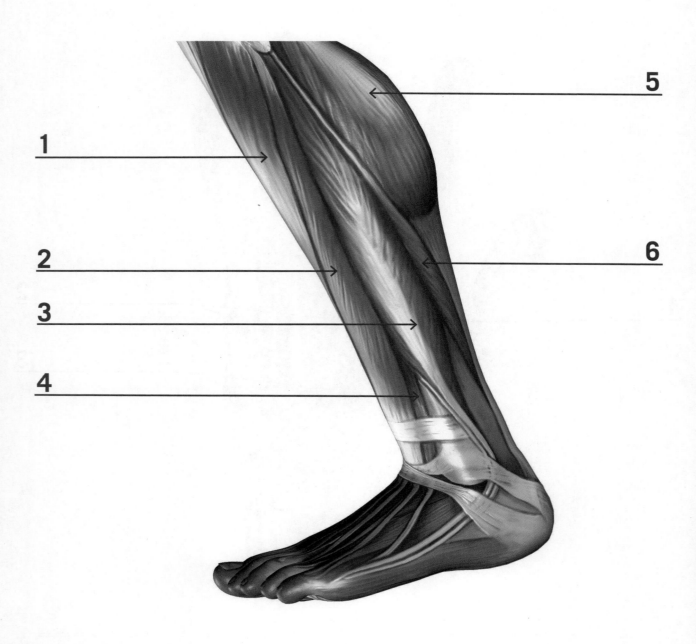

1. covers the front of the shin and bends the foot

2. the longer of the two muscles responsible for rotating the foot down and out

3. the key stabilizing muscle of the lower leg and helps the foot to flex inward

4. the shorter of the two muscles responsible for rotating the foot down and out

5. a muscle located in the calf that pulls the foot down; it is attached to the lower portion of the heel

6. a muscle that is attached to the lower heel; it stabilizes the leg and pulls the foot down

# MUSCLES OF THE FEET

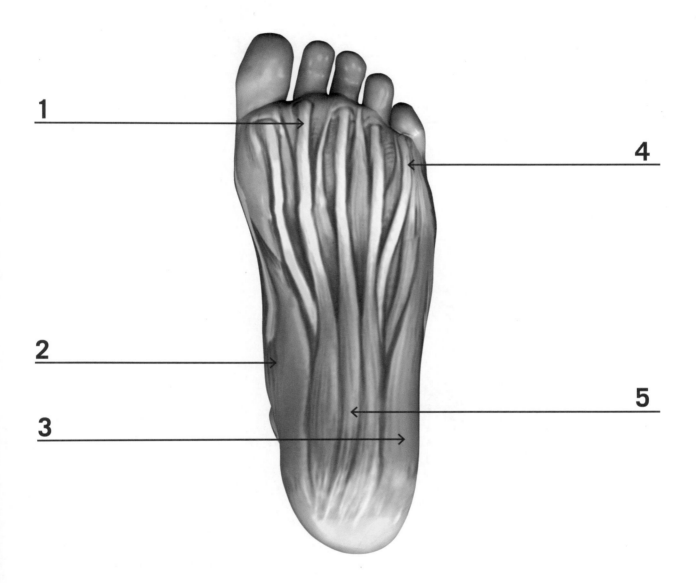

**1**

**2**

**3**

**4**

**5**

1. provide straightening or stretching and extend the toes

2. moves the foot away from the body and spreads the toes

3. moves the foot towards the body and draws the toes together

4. muscle that controls the little toe

5. helps to support the extensors by keeping the toes straight

# NERVES OF THE ARMS AND HANDS

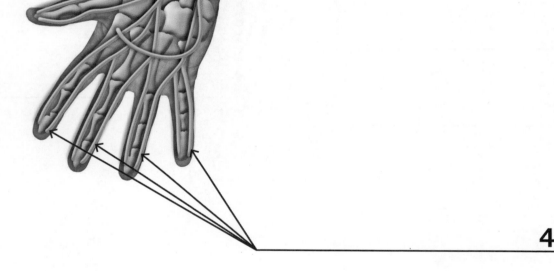

1

2

3

4

---

**1.** the smallest of the 3 arm and hand nerves

**2.** runs along the thumb side and back of the hand

**3.** runs along the pinky side and palm of the hand

**4.** located in the fingers and toes

# NERVES OF THE
# LEGS AND FEET

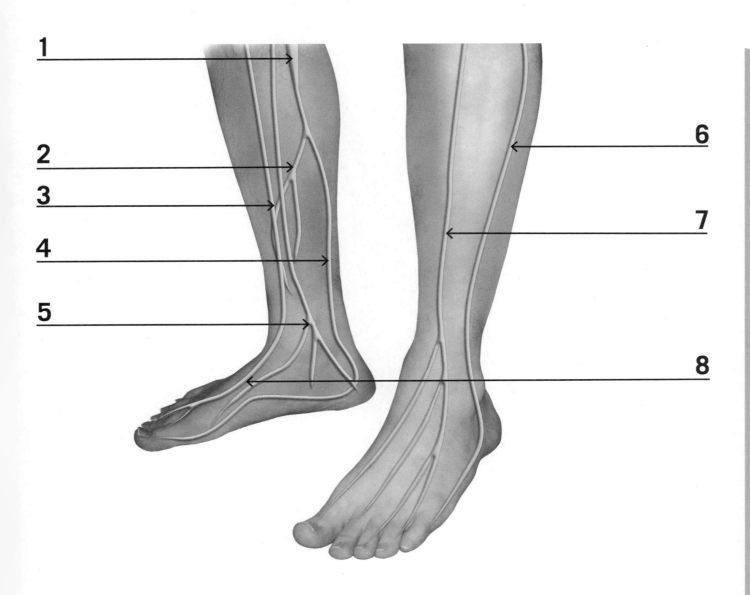

**1**

**2**

**3**

**4**

**5**

**6**

**7**

**8**

1. longest and largest nerve in the body

2. a division of the sciatic nerve that starts behind the knee; wraps to the front of the fibula

3. supplies impulses to the top of the foot and the first and second toes

4. runs behind the knee; supplies impulses to the calf muscle, heel, sole, skin of leg, knee and bottom of toes

5. supplies impulses for the inner side of the leg

6. supplies impulses for the outer side and back of the foot and leg

7. also known as the musculocutaneous nerve

8. part of the sapheneous nerve

# CIRCULATION OF THE ARMS AND HANDS

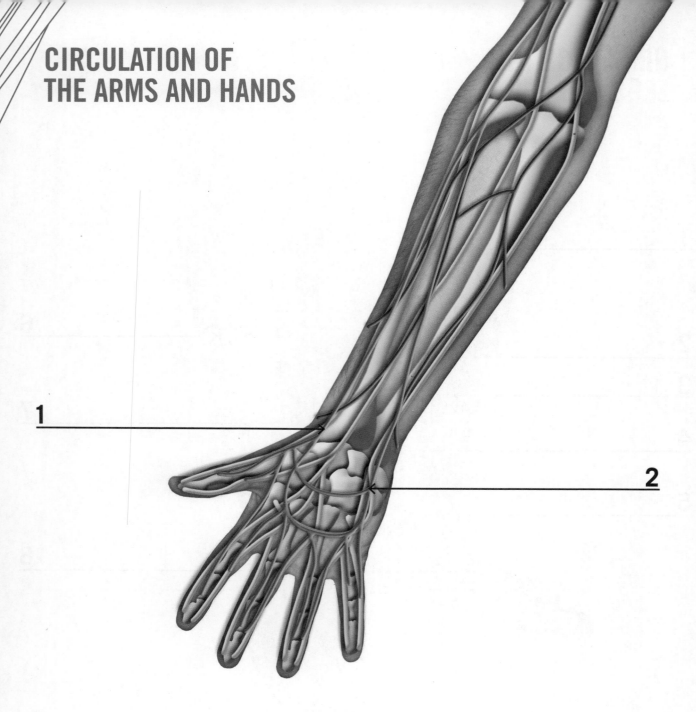

**1** ──────────────────────────────→

**2**

←────────────────────── **2**

**1.** supplies blood to the thumb side of the arm and back of the hand

**2.** supplies blood to the pinky side of the arm and the palm of the hand

# CIRCULATION OF THE LEGS AND FEET

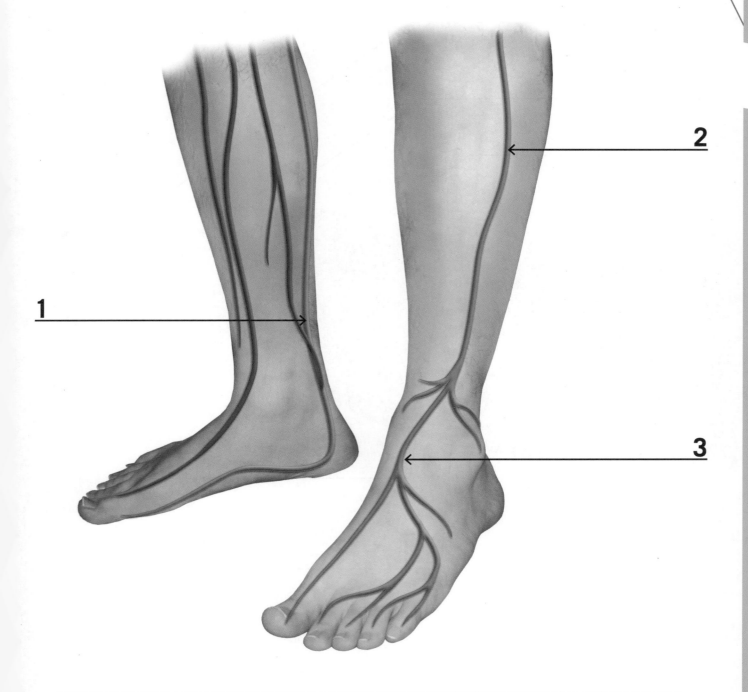

**1.** supplies blood to the ankle and back of the lower leg

**2.** supplies blood to the muscles of the lower leg, the skin and the top of the foot

**3.** supplies blood to the foot

# NAIL ANATOMY

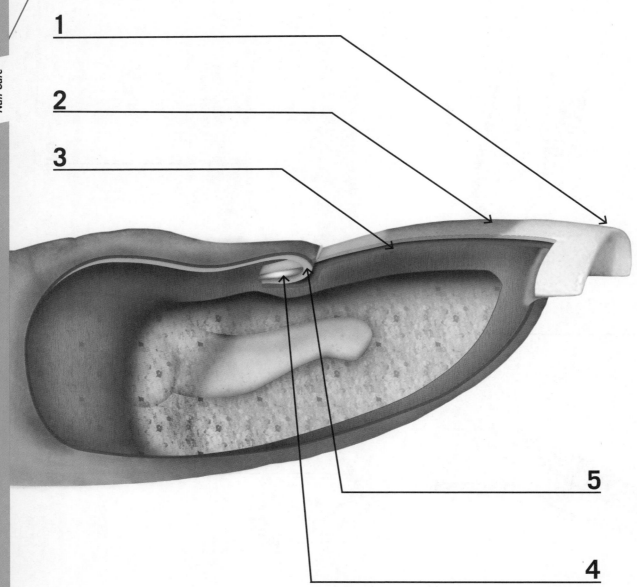

**1.** part of the nail plate that extends beyond the fingertip

**2.** translucent portion of the nail; also known as the nail body

**3.** portion of the skin that the nail plate rests upon as it grows out

**4.** part of the nail plate hidden under the mantle

**5.** pocket-like fold of skin that holds the nail root and matrix

# NAIL ANATOMY

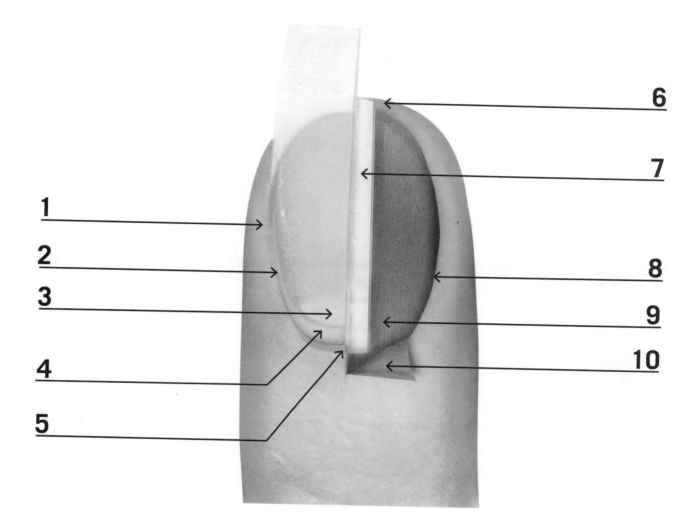

**1.** __ **6**

**2.** __ **7**

**3.** __ **8**

**4.** __ **9**

**5.** __ **10**

**1.** also known as the lateral nail fold

**2.** additional or excessive skin that overlaps onto the sides of the nail plate

**3.** whitish, half-moon shape at the base of the nail

**4.** living skin at the base of the nail plate; partially overlaps the lunula

**5.** small portion of non-living skin extending around the base of the nail

**6.** skin located between the free edge and the fingertip

**7.** thin layer of skin between the nail bed and the nail plate

**8.** slits or grooves on the sides of the nail that allow for growth

**9.** part of the nail bed that extends below the nail root and helps to produce the nail plate

**10.** fold of normal skin that surrounds the natural nail plate

# DISORDERS AND DISEASES OF NAILS

Fill in the missing information.

| DISORDER | SIGN / SYMPTOM | CAUSE(S) | ⚕ |
|---|---|---|---|
| Name:_____ | | | YES / NO |
| Name:_____ | | | YES / NO |
| Name:_____ | | | YES / NO |
| Name:_____ | | | YES / NO |
| Name:_____ | | | YES / NO |

| DISORDER | SIGN / SYMPTOM | CAUSE(S) | ⚕ |
|---|---|---|---|
| Name:_____ | | | **YES / NO** |
| Name:_____ | | | **YES / NO** |
| Name:_____ | | | **YES / NO** |
| Name:_____ | | | **YES / NO** |
| Name:_____ | | | **YES / NO** |
| Name:_____ | | | **YES / NO** |

# NAIL DISEASES | WORD SEARCH

1. _____ an inflammation of the nail matrix

2. _____ loosening of the nail plate without shedding

3. _____ also known as Tinea Unguium; a fungal infection of the nail

4. _____ a general term for any disease or deformity

5. _____ the technical term for nails

6. _____ a bacterial inflammation of the skin that surrounds the nail plate

7. _____ granuloma are small round masses of vascular tissue that project from the nail bed to the nail plate

8. _____  _____ also known as Athlete's Foot; a fungal infection that can occur on the feet and/or toes and spread to the toenails

# NAIL DISEASES | WORD SEARCH

```
H  J  Y  X  J  O  Q  X  W  S  S  H  U  Y  S
E  C  L  I  E  N  O  P  E  I  W  P  F  W  A
Q  J  N  D  M  Y  L  N  S  S  Y  O  D  Y  U
R  F  P  M  C  C  U  Y  T  O  X  Q  R  B  H
E  V  N  J  X  H  L  E  G  C  C  Y  R  Y  K
T  T  Z  K  E  O  F  E  S  Y  H  P  N  Y  K
P  I  T  L  H  S  N  S  S  M  O  V  G  O  B
V  O  N  C  Y  I  Y  O  H  O  B  V  P  L  B
O  I  Y  E  C  S  N  C  D  H  Z  V  O  M  S
S  N  H  P  A  R  O  N  Y  C  H  I  A  S  G
O  O  K  K  W  P  N  E  K  Y  I  E  K  M  F
O  M  Q  N  L  S  E  N  M  N  W  O  Y  T  W
A  I  H  C  Y  N  O  D  M  O  U  O  M  V  I
J  C  D  J  T  V  L  Z  I  K  M  C  O  L  J
Q  R  D  Q  C  Q  N  X  I  S  D  Q  V  U  C
```

# NAIL PRODUCT CHEMISTRY

A. Curing

B. Inhibition Layer

C. Photoinitiators

D. Initiators

E. Polymerization

F. Urethane Methacrylate

G. Monomer

H. Oligomers

I. Cyanoacrylates

J. Polymer

1._____ the chemical reaction that creates polymers, also known as curing or hardening

2._____ main ingredient used to create UV gel nail enhancements

3._____ the chemical that begins the polymerization process in gel nails

4._____ a concentrate made up of acrylic powder that when mixed with a monomer forms a nail enhancement

5._____ short polymer chains that consist of just a few monomers, creating a thickened resin or a 'gel-like' substance

6._____ liquid that mixes with acrylic powder and binds the acrylic polymers to form a nail enhancement

7._____ substances that begin the process of starting the chain reaction, leading to very long polymer chains being created

8._____ the sticky, film-like layer that forms on the top of the nail enhancement

9._____ specialized acrylic monomers that quickly polymerize with the addition of alcohol, water or any weak alkaline product to form an adhesive

10._____ also known as polymerization, is the chemical reaction that causes hardening

# NAIL SHAPES | Draw and describe each of the five nail shapes.

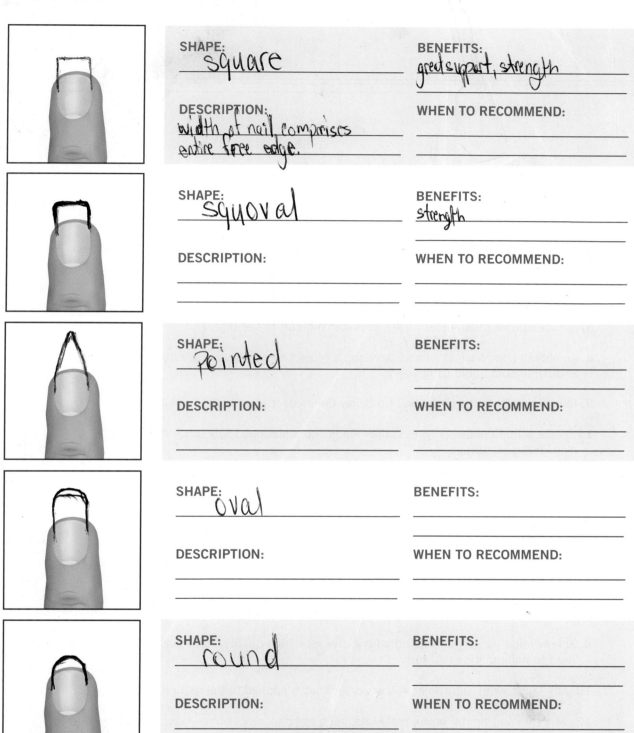

**SHAPE:** square

**BENEFITS:** great support, strength

**DESCRIPTION:** width of nail comprises entire free edge.

**WHEN TO RECOMMEND:**

---

**SHAPE:** squoval

**BENEFITS:** strength

**DESCRIPTION:**

**WHEN TO RECOMMEND:**

---

**SHAPE:** Pointed

**BENEFITS:**

**DESCRIPTION:**

**WHEN TO RECOMMEND:**

---

**SHAPE:** oval

**BENEFITS:**

**DESCRIPTION:**

**WHEN TO RECOMMEND:**

---

**SHAPE:** round

**BENEFITS:**

**DESCRIPTION:**

**WHEN TO RECOMMEND:**

---

## What are the factors you need to consider when determining the best nail shape for your Guest.

1. _____
2. _____
3. _____
4. _____
5. _____
6. _____

## DOWN

**1.** name for the edge of the well that bumps up against the free edge of the natural nail

**3.** this can occur to nails during filing or when removing the cuticle, causing small unseen openings in the skin

**4.** the main ingredient used to create UV gel nail enchancements

**5.** a thick or dark quality that makes products difficult to see through

**6.** an abbreviation for methyl methacrylate; a type of monomer that is a colorless, volatile and flammable liquid compound

**9.** this area is the edge of the nail tip below the contact area

**11.** process that creates polymers, then stops and a hardened substance is formed; also known as curing

## ACROSS

**2.** liquid solution that is applied sparingly to the natural nail plate prior to acrylic product application to assist in adhesion of the enhancement

**7.** the catalyst that helps quicken the drying time of the nail wrap resin

**8.** abbreviation for acrylonitrile butadiene styene; a high-quality virgin plastic, used to manufacture nail tips

**10.** any fabric wrap, ultraviolet gel, or acrylic that is applied to the natural nail

**12.** very thin and tightly woven materials, such as linen, silk or fiberglass, that are used to strengthen the natural nail or strengthen nail tips

**13.** this type of fabric wrap is made of a thin natural material with a tight weave that provides a smooth, even, clear appearance

**14.** a patch applied to cover a break or crack in the nail

# DEVELOPING YOUR NAIL CARE COMMUNICATION AND SOLUTION SKILLS

What consultation question(s) would you have prepared to ask your Guest about the following:

Manicure:_____

_____

Pedicure:_____

_____

Nail Enhancement:_____

_____

_____

Your Guest arrives for their scheduled nail enhancement maintenance. You notice a green spot between their nail plate and the overlay. What could this be and how should you handle it?

_____

_____

The nail shape and length your Guest is requesting is not the look you would recommend. What suggestions could you give?

_____

_____

You notice warts on the bottom of your Guest's foot. How should you approach this with your Guest?

_____

_____

# SERVICE RECOMMENDATIONS

Treatment options:_____

_____

Length and/or shape options:_____

_____

Creative nail design options:_____

_____

Type of nail polish:_____

_____

# MAINTENANCE RECOMMENDATIONS

When discussing a maintenance routine with your Guest, how often will you suggest they rebook for the following services?

Manicure: _____

Pedicure: _____

Nail Enhancements: _____

# PRODUCT RECOMMENDATIONS

Nail polish choice and why:_____

_____

Nail treatment choice and why:_____

_____

# WORKSHOP
# standards

**MET SKILL**

## Safety and Infection Control:

Disinfect work station *(before and after each service)*

Set up work station with required, clean service tools

## Consultation:

Nail Analysis:  ☐oily  ☐normal  ☐dry

Discuss nail shape:  ☐square  ☐round  ☐oval  ☐squoval  ☐pointed

Discuss nail length:  ☐short  ☐medium  ☐long

Desired polish color

## Procedure: *Manicure / Pedicure*

Begin by allowing your Guest's fingers / feet to soak for approximately 5 minutes

Remove polish

Cut and/or shape free edge

Apply cuticle remover

Soak fingers / feet in cleansing treatment

Remove left hand / foot from soak and dry

Gently push back cuticles

Carefully cut cuticle from the nail using cuticle nipper

Clean under free edge with cotton-wrapped manicure stick

Apply cuticle cream / oil at cuticle area

Remove right hand / foot from soak and dry

Repeat above steps on right hand / foot

Apply lotion to left hand / foot for massage; repeat on right hand / foot

Remove oily residue from the nail plate with cotton saturated in nail polish remover

## Finishing of Service:

Apply base coat starting with left hand / foot

Apply two coats of color polish

Clean excess polish off of skin

Apply top coat

Allow Guest to stay seated until nails are dry (approximately 10 to 15 minutes)

Recommend at-home maintenance product(s)

# MY NEED TO KNOW notes:

# SITUATIONAL SCENARIOS

1. One of your daily closing routines is proper cleaning of the pedicure area, which includes two whirlpool foot spas. What steps should you take to ensure the pedicure area and foot spas are ready for tomorrow's appointments?

   a) Remove filter screen, clean filter, clean basin with a disinfectant and a chelating soap. Next, drain, rinse and refill basin with water and a disinfectant, then let sit for 5 to 10 minutes before rinsing and drying

   b) Fill basin with a disinfectant; let sit for 5 to 10 minutes before rinsing and drying

   c) Fill the basin with water and circulate through system for 10 minutes; rinse and dry

   d) Scrub basin and filter for any visible residue with a chelating soap; fill tub with water, let sit for 10 minutes, rinse and dry

2. Two weeks ago you recommended and performed a gel nail polish service. How will you properly remove the gel nail polish during the maintenance service?

   a) Soak nails in a non-acetone remover for 10 to 15 minutes

   b) Soak nails in alcohol for 10 to 15 minutes

   c) Soak nails in an acetone remover for 10 to 15 minutes

   d) Soak nails in a monomer for 10 to 15 minutes

3. During a pedicure, you notice that your Guest's nail plate is abnormally thick. How should you proceed?

   a) Explain to your Guest you are unable to service them at this time and recommend they see a medical professional

   b) Avoid any nail service on that particular nail and continue with the pedicure

   c) Secure nail in an antiseptic soak wrap and continue with the pedicure service

   d) File nail down to a flat surface and/or buff the nail to a shine and continue with the pedicure service

4. Ann, your regular Guest, calls you an hour after her manicure and explains that her polish smudged on one of her nails. How should you proceed?

   a) Explain to Ann that you cannot guarantee the longevity of the polish

   b) Invite Ann to come back to the salon and fix the nail polish at no cost

   c) Explain to Ann it is her fault but you will fix the nail polish; however, she will be charged for a polish change

   d) Complain to Ann that she should have made sure her nails were completely dry before leaving the salon; therefore, you will not fix the nail polish

5. You have back-to-back manicure appointments and need to prepare your tools for the day. What tools are considered disposable and must be replaced?

   a) Nail brush and manicure bowl

   b) Soiled cotton and wooden pushers

   c) Cuticle nippers and metal cuticle pusher

   d) Nail tips and curette

**6.** When performing a nail enhancement application on your Guest, you notice that the acrylic is drying with visible crystals. What could be the cause?

    **a)** Product is contaminated
    **b)** Product was exposed to extreme temperatures
    **c)** Their hands are cold
    **d)** All of the above

**7.** During the consultation, your Guest tells you she loves to change her polish weekly but has noticed recently that her nails are yellow. What is a possible cause?

    **a)** Heart condition
    **b)** Vitamin deficiency
    **c)** Polish stains
    **d)** Minor trauma

**8.** Mark asked for the calluses on his heels to be smoothed. What tool / product will you need to achieve the desired results?

    **a)** Exfoliating scrub
    **b)** Foot file
    **c)** Callus softener
    **d)** All of the above

**9.** Your Guest just received a fill. She calls the next day because her nails are lifting. How can you prevent this from happening again?

    **a)** Explain to your Guest that they should wait at least 3 to 4 weeks before having a fill
    **b)** When performing the fill, make sure the acrylic consistency is dry and chalky
    **c)** Always use gel instead of acrylic product
    **d)** Ensure the following: proper preparation, product consistency and proper application

**10.** You notice inflammation of the skin surrounding the nail plate but no pus is present. What could be the cause?

    **a)** Paronychia
    **b)** Pyogenic Granuloma
    **c)** Onycholysis
    **d)** Tinea pedis

**11.** To buff the nails to a high shine, you need to finish filing with what grit range?

    **a)** 180 to 240
    **b)** 240 to 400
    **c)** 400 to 899
    **d)** 900 to 1200

**12.** Beth, a first time Guest, has thin, flexible, average length nails. Recently, her nails have been breaking; she would like to shape her nails to provide support and strength while they grow. Into what shape should you file Beth's nails?

    **a)** Oval
    **b)** Round
    **c)** Square
    **d)** Pointed

# practical PREP

*Each skill will be checked by your Educator and feedback will be provided.*
*Met Skill = 1 point / Not Met Skill = 0 points*

Nail Care

**POINTS**

## Safety and Disinfection:

Disinfects work station *(before and after each service)*

Station set up with required tools

Uses disinfected or disposable implements

Applies gloves

Performs nail analysis

**Feedback:**

## Manicure Procedure:

Begins manicure on left hand

Files free edge from outer edge corner to center on all nails

Soaks fingers in cleansing treatment

Removes and dries fingers and hand

Applies cuticle cream or oil with disposable applicator

Gently pushes back cuticles

Using nail brush, brushes nails from cuticle area out toward the free edge

Cleans under free edge with cotton-wrapped manicure stick

Buffs nails gently and safely

Applies massage cream, starting at tip of littlest finger massaging in circular motion, moving up the finger to top of and underneath of the hand

Removes oily residue from nail plate with cotton saturated in nail polish remover

Applies base coat to all nails (starting with left hand)

Applies two coats of color polish to all nails evenly and smoothly

Cleans any excess polish off skin using cotton-wrapped manicure stick saturated with nail polish remover

Applies one coat of top coat to all nails

**Feedback:**

# NAIL CARE
## STATE BOARD THEORY REVIEW

1. An activator is a catalyst to help quicken the _____ of nail wrap resins:

   a) drying time        b) spreading          c) softening          d) all the above

2. _____ hydrogen peroxide is a disinfectant that only needs to be changed every 14 days:

   a) Barbicide          b) Quaternary         c) Accelerated        d) Phenol

3. Acrylonitrile butadiene _____ is a high-quality virgin plastic used to make artificial nail tips:

   a) polymer            b) styrene            c) compound           d) none of the above

4. The adductor muscles pull fingers and/or toes:

   a) apart              b) together           c) away               d) open

5. A licensed professional refers to the split cuticle around the nail as:

   a) agnail / hangnail  b) loose skin         c) overgrowth         d) eponychium

6. The muscles that spread fingers and/or toes:

   a) abductors          b) extensors          c) adductors          d) flexors

7. Visible depressions running the width of the natural nail plate are a nail condition called _____ lines:

   a) Beau's             b) bruised            c) bowed              d) folded

8. Alcohol is extremely:

   a) thick              b) favorable          c) flammable          d) opaque

9. _____ is also known as polymerization:

   a) Application        b) Smoothing          c) Curing             d) Removal

10. The bed epithelium is the thin layer of skin cells between the nail bed and the nail:

   a) plate              b) grooves            c) matrix             d) free edge

11. A bruised nail has a dark purplish discoloration under the nail and can:

   a) not be serviced    b) be serviced with   c) be filed down      d) none of the above
                            gentle pressure

12. _____ soaps help break down and remove the residue from foot soaks, scrubs and masks:

a) Chelating     b) Bacterial     c) Sanitary     d) Deodorant

13. The small portion of non-living skin extending around the base of the nail:

a) cortex     b) medulla     c) cuticle     d) loose skin

14. The technical term for the 8 bones that form the wrist:

a) wrist bones     b) carpals     c) tarsals     d) arm and hand bones

15. _____ are also known as phalanges:

a) Carpals     b) Femur     c) Digits     d) Fibula

16. A disorder of the nail characterized by a thin, white nail plate that is more flexible than normal:

a) brittle     b) bitten     c) eggshell     d) bruised

17. Cyanoacrylates are specialized acrylic monomers that quickly polymerize with the addition of alcohol or water to form a/an:

a) adhesive     b) polish     c) wrap     d) none of the above

18. The technical term for the thigh bone:

a) femur     b) fibula     c) flexor     d) fingers

19. The living skin that overlaps the lunula:

a) eponychium     b) humerus     c) leukonychia     d) onychia

20. Extensor muscles cause joints to _____ and body parts to stretch:

a) straighten     b) bend     c) cramp     d) all of the above

21. The nerves located in the fingers and toes are called:

a) radial nerves     b) median nerves     c) ulnar nerves     d) digital nerves

22. Fabric wraps are made from linen, silk or:

a) fiberglass     b) paper     c) plastics     d) wood

23. Flexor muscles cause joints to _____ and fingers and wrists to curl:

   a) straighten     b) bend     c) cramp     d) all of the above

24. The _____ is the part of the nail plate that extends beyond the fingertip:

   a) free edge     b) matrix     c) median     d) bed

25. The flexor digiti minimi muscle controls the:

   a) little toe     b) finger     c) ring finger     d) large toe

26. The bone that forms the outer part of the lower leg, from the knee to the ankle:

   a) femur     b) fibula     c) flexor     d) finger

27. The gastrocnemius muscle pulls the foot:

   a) up     b) over     c) down     d) sideways

28. The _____ is the largest bone in the upper arm, extending from the shoulder to the elbow:

   a) tibia     b) fibula     c) tarsal     d) humerus

29. Hardening is also known as:

   a) curing     b) accelerating     c) neutralizing     d) processing

30. The hyponychium is located _____ the free edge:

   a) above     b) on top of     c) under     d) beside

31. The substances that start the chain reaction creating long polymer chains:

   a) inhibition     b) initiators     c) gastrocnemius     d) photoinitiators

32. A lateral nail fold is also known as nail:

   a) beds     b) sidewalls     c) grooves     d) plates

33. The sign(s) and/or symptom(s) of leukonychia:

   a) white spots     b) dark spots     c) green spots     d) all of the above

34. The inhibition layer is a _____, film-like layer that forms on top of the nail enhancement:

   a) tacky          b) rough          c) smooth          d) dry

35. Lungs are the spongy, respiratory organs that are responsible for exhaling and:

   a) inhaling          b) lifting          c) moving          d) smelling

36. The half-moon shape at the base of the nail is known as the:

   a) matrix          b) lunula          c) onyx          d) phenol

37. The mantle is a pocket-like fold of skin that holds the nail root and the:

   a) matrix          b) root          c) lunula          d) onyx

38. The smallest of the three arm and hand nerves:

   a) median          b) microtrauma          c) longus          d) brevis

39. To care for the hands and fingernails by cutting, shaping, polishing and softening:

   a) tip application          b) pedicure          c) manicure          d) massage

40. The part of the nail bed that extends below the nail root and helps to produce the nail plate is the:

   a) onyx          b) matrix          c) nail bed          d) nail groove

41. Melanonychia is a _____ of the nails caused by excess melanin:

   a) lightening          b) darkening          c) elongating          d) shortening

42. Metatarsals contain _____ slender bones located between the ankles and the feet:

   a) 3          b) 5          c) 9          d) 2

43. A metal pusher is used to gently _____ the cuticle from the nail plate:

   a) force          b) remove          c) scrape          d) smooth

44. There are _____ metacarpals between the wrist and fingers that form the palm of the hand:

   a) 3          b) 4          c) 2          d) 5

# NAIL CARE
## STATE BOARD THEORY REVIEW

45. Methyl Methacrylate is a type of _____ that is a colorless, volatile and flammable liquid compound:

a) monomer    b) polymer    c) polish    d) adhesive

46. The liquid that mixes with acrylic powder to form a nail enhancement:

a) polymer    b) monomer    c) developer    d) peroxide

47. Causing small unseen openings in the skin that allow for the entry of pathogens:

a) manicure    b) microtrauma    c) polish    d) dehydrates

48. The nail plate rests upon this portion of the skin:

a) nail wall    b) eponychium    c) nail bed    d) paronychia

49. Nail folds surround the natural nail:

a) plate    b) bed    c) wall    d) free edge

50. Nail dehydrator removes _____ or oils from the nail plate:

a) dirt    b) debris    c) moisture    d) residue

51. Nail _____ are the slits on the sides of the nail that allow forward growth:

a) grooves    b) plate    c) wall    d) free edge

52. Nail psoriasis is a non-infectious condition that appears _____ and rough:

a) shiny    b) natural    c) pink    d) pitted

53. The translucent portion of the nail that extends from the nail root to the free edge:

a) nail grooves    b) nail plate    c) nail wall    d) nail fold

54. Onyx is the technical term for:

a) nail    b) skin    c) free edge    d) cuticle

55. Nail pterygium is the forward growth of living skin that adheres to the:

a) nail bed    b) nail plate    c) nail wall    d) free edge

56. The nail _____ is the portion of the nail plate hidden under a fold of skin (mantle) at the base of the nail plate:

   a) bed      b) root      c) rasp      d) grooves

57. Onychauxis is the noticeable _____ of the fingernails or toenails:

   a) thinning      b) overgrowth      c) swelling      d) disorder

58. Nail wrap _____ is used to adhere the fabric wrap:

   a) resin      b) polish      c) oil      d) glue

59. Short polymer chains, known as _____, create a thickened resin:

   a) oligomers      b) onychorrhexis      c) opponens      d) onyx

60. The nail _____ are the pieces of skin that overlap onto the side of the nail:

   a) sidewalls      b) folds      c) grooves      d) bed

61. Onychatrophia is also known as _____ of the fingernails or toenails:

   a) onyx      b) atrophy      c) opponens      d) ringworm

62. Opacity is the thick or _____ quality that makes something hard to see through:

   a) dark      b) light      c) translucent      d) transparent

63. Onychia is the inflammation of the nail:

   a) plate      b) wall      c) bed      d) matrix

64. The loosening or separation of the nail plate without shedding:

   a) onychia      b) onyx      c) onycholysis      d) opponens

65. Onychophagy is a technical term used for _____ nails:

   a) ingrown      b) bitten      c) brittle      d) loss

66. Onychorrhexis is the abnormal _____ of the nail plate:

   a) softening      b) lengthening      c) brittleness      d) oiliness

# NAIL CARE
## STATE BOARD THEORY REVIEW

67. Onychosis is the general term for any nail:

a) disease      b) fungus      c) enhancement      d) disorder

68. The opponens is a group of adductor muscles that pulls the thumb _____ the fingers:

a) towards      b) away      c) opposite of      d) behind

69. Onychocryptosis is the technical term for a/an _____ nail:

a) ingrown      b) agnail      c) split      d) thick

70. An overlay product used in a nail service:

a) fabric wrap      b) ultraviolet gel      c) acrylic / sculptured      d) all of the above

71. Onychomycosis is a fungal infection of the nail, also known as:

a) tinea unguium      b) onychophagy      c) onycholysis      d) opponens

72. The bacterial inflammation of the skin surrounding the nail plate:

a) paronychia      b) eponychium      c) nail bed      d) hyponychium

73. Patella is the technical term for the:

a) elbow      b) knuckles      c) kneecap      d) wrists

74. Onychomadesis is the complete _____ of the nail:

a) shedding      b) re-growth      c) overgrowth      d) discoloration

75. Pedicure is the cosmetic care of the toenails and:

a) hands      b) arms      c) face      d) feet

76. The perioncychium is the additional or excessive skin that overlaps onto the sides of the nail:

a) plate      b) wall      c) folds      d) grooves

77. The peroneus longus are responsible for rotating the foot:

a) down and out      b) up and out      c) in and down      d) none of the above

78. A strong, high pH disinfectant used in the salon:

a) phenol     b) alcohol     c) quats     d) antiseptic

79. _____ are the chemicals that begin the polymerization process in gel nails:

a) Nail wrap resins     b) Photoinitiators     c) Activators     d) All of the above

80. Plicatured nail plates are folded into the nail bed at a/an _____ angle:

a) 0 degrees     b) 45 degrees     c) 90 degrees     d) 180 degrees

81. Peroneus brevis is the shorter of the two muscles responsible for rotating the:

a) shoulders     b) knees     c) hands / arms     d) foot / feet

82. When mixed with a monomer, the powder that forms a nail enhancement:

a) polymer     b) polymerization     c) pronator     d) photoinitiator

83. Quaternary ammonium compounds are also known as:

a) ammonia     b) mixtures     c) quats     d) wet disinfection

84. Position stop is the edge of the well that bumps up against the _____ of the natural nail:

a) wall     b) base     c) plate     d) free edge

85. The _____ muscle turns the hand inward so the palm faces downward:

a) pronator     b) supinator     c) adductor     d) flexor

86. The radial artery supplies blood to the thumb side of the arm and _____ of the hand:

a) little finger side of the arm     b) palm of the hand     c) back     d) middle

87. Pyogenic Granuloma is a _____ that is caused by an infection or injury to the nail:

a) disorder     b) disease     c) infection     d) tissue

88. The radial nerve runs along the _____ side of the arm and the back of the hand:

a) thumb     b) little finger     c) middle finger     d) none of the above

# NAIL CARE
## STATE BOARD THEORY REVIEW

89. _____ assists in nail enhancement adhesion:

a) Acrylic    b) Primer    c) Nail polish    d) All of the above

90. The radius bone is located on the _____ side of the forearm:

a) pinky    b) middle finger    c) index finger    d) thumb

91. Tibia is the technical term for the _____ bone:

a) femur    b) patella    c) shin    d) fibula

92. _____ is based on the use of reflex points located throughout the body:

a) Dermatology    b) Endocrinology    c) Aromatherapy    d) Reflexology

93. Sodium hypochlorite is commonly known as:

a) alcohol    b) ammonia    c) bleach    d) detergent

94. _____ are caused by matrix injury, excessive use of cuticle and polish removers and run the length or width of the nail plate:

a) Ridges    b) Furrows    c) Corrugations    d) All of the above

95. A _____ patch is used in the event that a nail has been broken or cracked:

a) repair    b) polymer    c) gel    d) acrylic

96. _____ wraps are made from thin material having a tight weave to create a smooth, even, clear appearance:

a) Silk    b) Paper    c) Fiberglass    d) Wood

97. Ringworm is a contagious _____ infection:

a) fungal    b) parasitic    c) host    d) blood

98. The soleus muscle is attached to the lower _____ and bends the foot down:

a) arm    b) heel    c) leg    d) knee

99. There are _____ tarsal bones that form the ankle:

a) 7    b) 8    c) 12    d) 5

# NAIL CARE
## STATE BOARD THEORY REVIEW

100. The _____ area is the edge of the nail tip below the contact area:

   a) work              b) free              c) side              d) stress

101. The muscle that turns the hand outward so the palm faces upward is known as the:

   a) supinator         b) inferior          c) superior          d) tibialis

102. The tibialis posterior is a muscle that helps the foot flex:

   a) upward            b) outward           c) inward            d) downward

103. Femur is the technical name for the _____ bone:

   a) shin              b) ankle             c) thigh             d) hip

104. The technical term for Athlete's Foot:

   a) tinea             b) tarsal            c) tibia             d) tinea pedis

105. The tibialis anterior muscle covers the shin and _____ the foot:

   a) bends             b) smooths           c) rotates           d) cramps

106. The ulna is the inner and larger bone on the outside of the forearm located on the:

   a) pinky side        b) middle finger     c) index finger      d) thumb side

107. Tinea, also known as ringworm, can be found anywhere on the:

   a) head              b) hands             c) feet              d) body

108. The ulnar artery supplies _____ to the little finger side of the arm and the palm of the hand:

   a) lymph             b) nourishment       c) water             d) blood

109. Urethane acrylate, the main ingredient used to create gel nails has little to no:

   a) odor              b) tackiness         c) color             d) opacity

110. Wrap Resin Accelerator, is also a/an _____ that speeds up the chemical reaction:

   a) activator         b) polymer           c) monomer           d) polish

111. The _____ nerve runs along the little finger side of the arm and the palm of the hand:

   a) ulnar             b) digital           c) median            d) frontal

112. Wooden pushers are made of which disposable wood materials:

   a) orange            b) rose              c) hard              d) all of the above

ATION DATE
'31/2016

Professional & Occupational Affairs

Nail Care